2017
EDITION

The **Business Owner's Guide** To The **UK's Best Accountancy Practices**

Shane Lukas

The **Business Owner's Guide** To The
UK's Best Accountancy Practices
Shane Lukas

Contents

Introduction – Why I Produced This Book

Every business owner, either of a start up or an established firm, needs help and support in growing their business and taking it to the next level. Nobody knows more about businesses and is in a better position to help them do this than an accountant. Sadly, too many accountants focus purely on producing a set of accounts that are of no real benefit to a business owner, they are simply a necessary evil, a legal requirement that business owners must adhere to, which means they have to seek out an accountant who will perform this valueless task for them. This devalues accountants.

There are a growing number of enlightened accountants who appreciate that although accounts may be a necessary evil, they have sought out additional training to repurpose their skills with numbers to help their business owner clients change the numbers that matter to them. These accountants have strong ethics and values around making a positive difference to people's lives; they've pledged their commitment to helping businesses grow and thrive.

Most business owners don't really know about these more forward thinking accountants. They don't know what untapped potential lies in their business. Most business owners are great at delivering their core operational service or product but have significant knowledge gaps in other areas of business like pricing, marketing, sales, financials, strategy, team building and creating scalability within their business in order to effectively grow it.

AVN Accountants have undergone a personal transformation themselves, want to do much more for their clients and are in a great position to do so because of their skills with numbers.

The purpose of this book is to provide insight to business owners about how working with an AVN Accountant can help their business in ways they've never previously experienced. It's also my hope that other accountants will want to step up and do much more for their clients when they come across this book too. In this book I'll share with you how a great accountant can really help you grow your business and change your personal life as a business owner so that you're spending less of your time working in the business and more time reaping the rewards of a great business and doing the stuff you want to do.

Who's This Book For?

This book is for anyone in business who...

- Uses an accountant every year to process their accounts and complete tax returns
- Wants to grow their business
- Wants more profit
- Wants to work fewer hours
- Wants to achieve a better lifestyle
- Wants to grow their personal wealth

You've probably heard the analogy of the frog that when placed in hot water jumps straight out because it's such a hostile environment. But the frog whose watery environment heats up gradually doesn't realise how bad things are getting until it's too late.

If you were to step outside of yourself and look in at your business and personal life as a third person, what would you see?

Is it the life you had in mind?

Is it where five years ago you'd expected to now be?

How hot is your water getting?

Is your business causing a relationship strain or is it likely to if things continue as they are?

Do you want to take your business to the next level and need some expertise and experience to help you do that?

Do you need to take back control of your life?

Everybody in business benefits from receiving strong external support and accountants can be a great source of experience, knowledge and insight.

Don't believe an accountant can help you with all of the above?

Read on...

How To Use This Book

The purpose of this book is to draw your attention as a business owner to possibilities, the help you're possibly missing out on and the impact that could be having on your business.

We Don't Know What We Don't Know

This book isn't intended to criticise your existing accountants. The last thing I want to do is take work away from them, but you as a business owner have an entitlement to great business advice and strategic input from your accountants. The difference that the accountants listed in this book can have on businesses large and small (including startups) is profound.

The second purpose of this book is for you to seek out an accountant who, as a bare minimum, delivers on the things I mention next. This book contains a directory listing of accountants who meet the standards described in this book. Each directory entry provides information about each accountant and the type of business they specialise in working with.

If your current accountant isn't giving you the time and the advice you need then it's worth consulting one of these accountants. A no obligation, exploratory conversation simply can't do any harm!

Coming up, there's further information about how these accountants can help you.

As I mentioned before, it's not my intention to hurt your current accountant and I've no doubt you'll have built up a relationship with them. It's possible, of course, that an assumption has been made that you don't need pro-active advice and recommendations; a conversation with your current accountant would be a great first step after reading this book.

Through reading this book there will be three possible outcomes:
1. You will do nothing.
2. You will talk to your existing accountant about working more closely with you in a strategic and truly proactive manner leading to sustainable business growth and high returns.
3. You will talk with one or more of the accountants listed in this book and judge for yourself if you're truly getting value from your current accountant.

22 Things To Expect From An Accountant (At The Very Least)

Accountants, through their training and experience, understand more than most about the mechanics of business. Whether long established or fledgling they are able to systematically offer and deliver on the following at the very least.

The General Support That You Should Expect

1. A fixed price agreed in advance of work being carried out with clear expectations about what will be done, what support is included and exactly which services and products are included with no unexpected bills at the end.

2. The ability to spread the payments over the period of the year so that your cash flow is better planned, avoiding the need to pay a lump sum in one go.

3. Your accountant should be on top of your financials and accounts and every year end meeting should include a list of recommendations for you to consider. These recommendations should be based on the experience of the accountant and how the environment is changing around us every single day together with those which will boost your cash flow, profits or simply make life easier for you.

4. Help you to identify the most important key metrics within your business that when focused upon, measured and managed, will lead to more effective growth and profitability.

5. Produce a personal balance sheet helping you establish the true value of your assets.

6. Analyse your sales pipeline and help you implement sales improvement strategies.

7. Benchmark your business against others in your industry. See how your competitors from around the UK compare to you in terms of their profits, cash flow, debtor days and many other important attributes. This helps identify the areas you can most easily improve.

8. Produce regular cash flow forecasts to ensure that your plans can be funded and that you don't fall into cash flow difficulties.

9. Attend regular meetings with you (and your business partners) bringing in to those meetings financial input, challenge, insight and questioning with a view to driving your business forward.

10. Develop and maintain an improvement action plan for your business based on the above, offering nagging and accountability in order to help you achieve your aspirations in business.

Strengthening Your Cash Flow By Making More Profitable Sales And Getting Paid More Quickly

11. Explore with you the eight key profit drivers, identifying which has the most potential for you and helping you develop strategies to improve on each of those important drivers.

12. Examine with you the eight sources of cash flow and explore the potential improvements in each area to keep cash in your bank rather than locked up.

13. Breakdown your sales figure into the seven key sales drivers, demonstrating how small tweaks to each of those key drivers can impact on the bottom line and then how combining the impact each of those individual tweaks can really raise profits.

14. Analyse your pricing strategy and work with you to increase your prices in ways that continue to win and retain customers.

15. Examine over 40 different ways to improve your debt collection systems.

Strengthening Your Business And Personal Cash Flow Through Proactive Tax Planning

NB. The following describe the benefits of quality tax planning, nothing referred to here is illegal. Paying taxes is important but in many cases poor tax planning means businesses pay far more tax than they need to which can be detrimental to the business. Proactive tax planning allows the business to invest into itself in order to grow.

16. Regularly examine the most tax efficient structure for your business that reduces your tax bills to the legal minimum you need to pay.

17. Help you incentivise and reward your key team member's tax efficiently.

18. Examine the most tax efficient route to draw your hard earned profits from your business so you only pay the legal minimum.

19. Help you to significantly reduce your incorporation tax bills.

20. Identify and reduce inheritance tax bills on estates to the legal minimum.

21. Defer, reduce and possibly eliminate capital gains tax liabilities through careful planning.

22. Inheritance tax and care home fee planning that will put extra cash in your bank during your lifetime.

Aren't Accountants All The Same?

To a large extent, yes, in that all accountants (legitimately qualified accountants) have the ability to produce your compliance accounts and tax returns. They can provide management accounts information and essentially offer a basic set of services to any business.

In my experience most accountants want to be able to do far more for their clients but because of the changing environment in which they operate they have become stuck in a rut.

There's a good chance that you sought out the cheapest accountant. You resent the fact that the government insists that your accounts and tax returns are submitted annually and the only people qualified to deal with this are accountants. It's a distraction and an expense you could do without. Right?

And as a result, you get your books and records over to your accountant either via your cloud accounting system, pass it over digitally or throw them your bag of invoices and dread the day they want to meet you to go through your accounts before submitting them since it's the most boring activity you've experienced to date.

And then… you get the bill from that accountant which is more than they told you it would be. You query it with them and they tell you about the unforeseen issues that they had to deal with; the call you made to them and the additional work they carried out for you. You didn't even realise that was going to be over and above. You expected it as part of the job. Now they just throw an invoice at you and expect you to pay it.

I don't blame you; most people do the same. Accounts that reflect the previous year aren't any use these days to anybody but the tax collector. Decades ago, when things moved at a much steadier pace it was useful to study the accounts of the previous year and identify areas that could be improved upon going forward. Now it's just outdated information.

The only role most accountants play is that they're simply processing those annual accounts like a production factory. They do this because they've allowed themselves to become cheap accountants, which means they're unable to justify any additional form of analysis, produce recommendations or spot problems before it's too late for you, the business owner.

What's An AVN Accountant?

Did you ever watch the film *Jerry Maguire*, a 1996 romantic comedy starring Tom Cruise, Cuba Gooding Jnr and Renée Zellweger? Jerry Maguire (Tom Cruise) is a typical sports agent. He's expected to work with an overwhelming amount of clients and as such is only able to give each very little of his time. This has become the norm. One night, Jerry has an epiphany about his role and writes a huge document that explains what's wrong with the way things currently are and how working with fewer clients and giving each much more time could lead to better quality outcomes for the athletes they work with.

He posts a copy of the document in every post box in his organisation and then goes to bed. The next morning he bottles it and tries to retrieve the documents before anyone sees them but he's far too late. As he walks in to the main office everybody cheers him and gives him a pat on the back whilst simultaneously knowing that he's just got himself dismissed. And he did.

The film goes on to show Jerry working with just one client, the American football player for the Arizona Cardinals, Rod Tidwell (Cuba Gooding Jnr). Over the duration of the film we see Jerry's relationship with his only client build despite many harsh criticisms between them about their respective shortcomings. He is able to work far more closely with Rod and focus on trying to get him the contract Rod really wants.

At the end of the film, when it's revealed that Rod has been offered this dream contract, he thanks Jerry live on TV, which in turn leads to other athletes wanting to work with Jerry.

I've skipped on the inevitable romantic part of the film for two reasons. Firstly, it's not relevant to the point I'm making here and secondly I don't want your eyes to get so teary that you can't read on.

An AVN accountant is an accountant who has chosen to work with fewer clients and give them far more quality; quality time, quality recommendations, quality advice.

An AVN accountant is the owner or partner of an accountancy practice who recognises that they too have a business to run, they too wish to enjoy life and get rewarded fairly for the work they do. They want to feel less stressed and actually enjoy running their business, just as I'm sure you do.

They've worked to get themselves out of the rut of being or becoming the cheap accountant because they want to be the valued accountant and trusted advisor who truly makes a positive difference to the businesses and the lives of the business owners they work with.

AVN accountants have undergone a transition in their practice. They've chosen to work with far fewer clients but deliver a higher quality of service. They work far more closely with those clients and use their great skills with numbers to cut through the fog of data and focus on what matters most.

The 22 things to expect from an accountant detailed in the previous chapter are all offered as part of the normal service by an AVN accountant. Many of those aspects are simply built in to the minimum service delivery as a matter of routine.

Because the business owners they work with see immediate benefits, they're happy to pay more for the additional support since the returns are so much more rewarding. You get what you pay for.

AVN accountants seek to understand what really matters to you and how your business is either complementing or hindering your personal life. Using their vast experience in business and that of changing their own circumstances for the better, they're able to help you develop a business that's profitable, successful and enjoyable to run. A business that gives you time to spend with family, friends or doing the stuff you really enjoy doing.

A Real Life Example

Here's an example of how an AVN accountant helped a typical business become something really special by working far more closely with their client. This case study is taken from the book 'The World's Most Inspiring Accountants' *(page 95).*

A 15 minute video is available on YouTube of both the accountant and the client recounting the story and it's incredible to see the bond between them. To watch it, click on the following link and select the Lewis Ballard story. (This playlist is made up of six similarly inspiring stories showing the impact that accountants can have on the businesses they work with).

http://bit.ly/29kg3Wq

"My accountant helped me build not just a business, but a family too." –Ben Matthew, a client of accounting firm Lewis Ballard

A four Director firm with a team of 16 based in Cardiff, Wales, which has helped a client:
- Avoid bankruptcy
- Develop a hugely successful business that is also compatible with family life
- Turned losses into a profit of £447,280
- Realise their dream of creating a cutting edge health and wellness centre for Wales

The client describes their impact as *"totally above and beyond what an accountant is expected to give."*

Ben Mathew is a chiropractor working in Cardiff. Originally introduced to chiropractic after a back injury, his ambitious goal was to enable the health of tens of thousands of people and inspire others with his passion for chiropractic care. He is married to Izzy, who also works for the business.

The Situation At The Start

Initially Ben was in partnership with another chiropractor, but the situation was far from ideal:

- He had signed a personal guarantee for a three year lease on a building that wasn't really suitable for their purposes
- They had no established patient list
- They had no financial systems
- There were no marketing strategies in place
- And no bank borrowing facility either

As a result, the partnership could not continue, and Ben faced personal bankruptcy.

The first thing Neil Ballard of Lewis Ballard did was to stabilise things by extracting Ben from the partnership and forming a new limited company so the lease could be renegotiated without the personal guarantee. He also secured an overdraft facility for the business.

The emotional impact of the predicament on Ben was significant. He was deeply hurt by the partnership problems and his confidence was seriously diminished. But his passion for chiropractic remained and his determination to succeed prevailed. So, with a loan from his parents, he decided to continue in business alone.

Initially he needed lots of support and guidance, with regular meetings and calls as Neil advised how to build up the business and recommended treatment plans and referral schemes to ensure repeat business and further growth.

By October 2009 the business had expanded to the extent that new premises with additional treatment rooms and an x-ray room were needed and also potentially another chiropractor to assist Ben. On Neil's advice, Izzy, Ben's wife, left her secure teaching job to work full time in the business.

How Their Accountants Helped – Part 1

Although business was booming there were underlying issues that meant Ben and Izzy were paying a high personal cost for their success. They were each working over 60 hours a week and the strain was affecting their physical and mental wellbeing.

So in October 2010 Neil invited them to a Lewis Ballard Focus Day to try to move forwards.

The Focus Day identified their key issues as:
- The business was not fully systemised so it was very dependent on Ben and Izzy being there
- They lacked management systems so it was difficult to measure and manage the business

- Izzy lacked confidence and experience in managing team issues
- Quarterly financial reporting was no longer adequate as the business grew
- There was no clear vision or purpose for the business that the team and patients could believe in
- Internal communication was poor and the business goals hadn't been shared with the team
- They lacked knowledge of the market and their competitors
- Ben found it uncomfortable to collect money from patients and gave too much away for free to avoid embarrassment. Debtors were also becoming a problem

Neil and the team from Lewis Ballard:
- Recommended that they reviewed the current team requirements, recruitment processes, job roles and training systems to develop a highly skilled and motivated team who were clear on what was expected and were confident to work without supervision. They also discussed how personal profiling could help find the right candidate for each job and showed them sample job roles
- Encouraged Izzy to prioritise time to immediately implement systems. As a result she quickly set up some of the key processes and the clinic immediately began to be run more efficiently
- Discussed at length the business manager role, helping Izzy to understand that she was entitled to want the best out of their business and should not be afraid to hold people accountable. As it was a new role she was going to experience some resistance, but in time she would gain trust and respect.

They gave her advice on how to deal with issues constructively and very quickly Izzy grew into her new role and was accepted by their team

- Trained Izzy on Cloud accounting software to produce monthly management figures so they could be reviewed to monitor progress and maintain control
- Helped to develop a draft mission statement. Once finalised this formed the basis of the clinic's message, ethos and core values
- Recommended regular team meetings to improve communication. Team members were encouraged to suggest improvements to systems or services, as they were best placed to assess where improvements can be made. They also supplied template feedback forms and suggested how to hold open meetings to encourage team spirit, participation and ideas. This resulted in a much greater team buy in
- Benchmarked the business to gain insights into the market and competition. They also supplied a template patient survey to help measure satisfaction and indicate areas for improvement or new services that could be provided
- De-personalised the payment of fees by suggesting that a price list was drawn up and adhered to. They also proposed creating a job sheet for any extra services so they could be priced at the time of consultation, but with the receptionist collecting the fees. This would help to avoid any costly gestures of kindness from Ben (something which had been a frequent and expensive issue in the past!). This immediately improved cash flow and almost simultaneously eliminated bad debt. The use of treatment plans and bundles also helped to ensure regular cash flow

Ben and Izzy had great plans for the business and wanted to develop additional services such as x-rays, orthotics, yoga and exercise classes. However, the business was still very reliant on them personally, and until the new systems and team were fully in place, they simply didn't have the capacity to cope with extra business. The Focus Day also highlighted the fact that they both wanted to start a family, but were anxious about how that would combine with the business. Neil reassured them that it was possible to have both, if they implemented the recommended changes.

Ben explained, *"I didn't know what to expect but this was the most valuable day of my life – both personally and for my business."* As a result of the Focus Day, Ben and Izzy started to build a business that wasn't so reliant on them being there. However, there were still some rocky times ahead...

Ben had taken on another chiropractor to free up his time for studying, developing cutting edge treatments and raising the profile of the business. Eventually, however, this employee had to be let go. This led to an unsuccessful but traumatic tribunal claim. Neil put them in touch with their own advisers who supported them through the tribunal and gave ongoing support with health and safety and employment law.

Recruitment of another associate was under way when Ben and Izzy announced that they were expecting their first child in July 2011. Although this made recruitment even more imperative, progress was slow. Ben decided that he would prefer to increase efficiencies and see more patients himself and then bring in an associate later in the year. So once again, the business became dependent on Ben. The situation was brought sharply into focus when the baby was born in May, three months prematurely. With a child in the neo-natal unit, Izzy was suddenly unable to manage the business and Ben's time was divided between the clinic and hospital.

For many months the family focus was on the health of their child and time was consumed by a string of hospital appointments. However, owing to the systems in place, the team pulling together and the strong loyalty of patients, the business survived this very difficult period. The treatment plans that had been implemented meant that patients remained loyal and payment methods ensured cash-flow maintained at a healthy level. Throughout this time, Lewis Ballard provided support to keep the business on track and gave guidance and friendship to help Ben and Izzy cope.

It took until June 2012 to find a suitable associate to join the business. Once he was in position and able to take on new referrals, Ben and Izzy's dream of a one-stop health and wellness centre became a real possibility. When they found a Listed period building that was ideal for conversion, Neil helped them to acquire funding, recommended solicitors and specialist surveyors, and also saved them £60,000 on their tax bill so they could purchase the property. As is the way with most building projects, the costs of the repairs escalated and Neil provided guidance, as well as helping them to raise further funding to complete the project and maximise further tax savings of £128,000 (through a Business Premises Renovation Allowance claim).

As a result, they proudly opened the doors of their state of the art new centre in January 2015.

The Difference It Made

In financial terms the impact on the business was huge:

- Accounts for September 2007 showed a loss of £25,000
- September 2008 – £27,000 net profit
- September 2009 – £132,618 net profit
- September 2010 – £191,264 net profit
- September 2012 – £229,922 net profit
- By 2014 net profit had reached £447,280

Monthly turnover is currently than for the whole of the first year, with monthly average takings for the first six months in their new clinic reaching £76,501. Their cash-flow is excellent.

Professionally they are now the leading clinic in Wales, employing eight people, and are developing a training programme to help graduates build their dream practices, so they too can inspire and change the health system in Wales.

Personally, Ben and Izzy have recently purchased their dream home and are now the proud parents of two beautiful children. They are both millionaires in their own right and have a financially secure future.

Lewis Ballard earn regular annual fees of £5,500 from the relationship, with additional projects averaging approximately £2,000 in most years. The firm's family and friends are regularly treated by Ben and Neil says, *"The difference to our health has been amazing. They have become friends and we have become their most trusted advisors. They always refer to us and always give us credit whenever possible."*

Perhaps even more significantly, when this story was told by Neil and Ben live on stage in September 2015 the delegates at the AVN National Accountants Conference voted Lewis Ballard as 'The UK's Most Inspiring Accountants.' Along with the title they also received a £10,000 cash prize sponsored by Xero.

As for Ben, over the years his standing and reputation as a chiropractor has grown dramatically and he is seen as a bright star of the profession who passionately champions the benefits of chiropractic care. In 2014 he attended an international chiropractic conference in Toronto and was awarded the international Chiropractic Community Rising Star award. In October 2015 he received the international UCA Chiropractor of the Year award and was invited to be the opening speaker at the next conference.

How It Made Them Feel

The emotional impact has been even greater than the financial impact. As Ben and Izzy wrote to Neil, *"What you do goes from basic accounting to life coaching – totally above and beyond what an accountant is expected to give. I don't have small aspirations and my wife and I are so glad that we have you in our lives as we have never taken a backward step in our business or private life in the time that we have known you. All that we have is because of you. You are really very special."*

What Can An AVN Accountant Do For You?

Most people who start a business do so because they have an idea about how they can deliver something that will make a difference to someone in some way. Most want to be able to deliver this in a way which complements their preferred lifestyle.

They typically want to achieve financial security, have a social life and enjoy family time as well as having time to pursue their hobbies. The reality is often very different. The business consumes their life and negatively affects their health, friendships and family.

Obviously building a business takes time and effort, but how much effort are you still putting in to your business? Is it giving you the lifestyle you wanted?

If you're not enjoying it, how can it be called success?

Of course, the help that an AVN accountant can give you is by no means limited to the 22 things listed in the previous chapter; I state those simply because they are offered routinely.

Central to the core offering of AVN accountants is the Performance Measurement and Improvement (PMI) system.

PMI measures where you are now and breaks down this measurement into key areas such as personal wealth, your business results, tax bills and the value of your business.

For each area your AVN accountant will work with you to identify your objectives and desired outcomes in these areas.
For example...

- What does financial security look like to you?
- How many hours per week would you prefer to be working in your business?
- What is the outcome for your business? Sell it? Hand it down?
- What would it need to be like to effectively do that?

Together you then drill down and identify the most important elements of those areas. The elements that, when you give them your focus, will have the biggest impact on those key metrics of personal wealth, business results, tax bills and business value.

Your AVN accountant then produces a One Page Plan consisting of those key metrics so that you only focus on the things that will have the biggest impact. This takes away the 'analysis paralysis' syndrome.

Because AVN accountants really understand the core mechanics of business they can use that expertise in conjunction with your knowledge of your own business to develop ideas that will change all of the numbers in the One Page Plan for the better.

The PMI process is often referred to as Sat Nav for business, and rather than continually looking backwards to the accounts of the previous year, it looks forward and helps you plot and continually tweak a route that leads to true success.

Of course, ideas are nothing without action and implementation.

It's easy to get sucked back into the day-to-day running of your business and that means you don't get time to make things happen. Your AVN accountant takes on the responsibility of collating actions, working with you to prioritise them effectively and will, if you wish, nag you and hold you accountable to those actions so that the results you seek happen.

The PMI system has been proven over and over again to be effective at helping businesses large and small, startup and long established, shift to a position where they are working for their owners – not the other way around.

Establishing a business that works for you means it doesn't rely on you for those day-to-day activities. You can shift your focus to strategy and growth. Your business will run effectively whilst you take as many holidays as you wish without taking your emails and phone calls with you. Can you see yourself doing that? How would that make you feel?

Are You Right For An AVN Accountant?

You may be wondering if your business is right for an AVN accountant.

Perhaps you're worried that you're not big enough or your business somehow doesn't have the potential to grow in the ways I've described.

AVN accountants aren't franchised; they're all individual firms sharing a common passion for helping UK businesses become the most successful and enjoyable to run in the world.

They each have a defined description of an ideal customer they choose to work with and most will not work with anyone who doesn't fit that description. The AVN accountants listed in this book have specified their ideal client profiles. These are generally fairly quick to glance through and read and I recommend doing just that.

With the technology available today it's not always necessary to work with an accountant in close proximity. Some are happy to travel to meet their clients, some effectively use technology to make distance irrelevant, and others prefer to work with clients in their local community.

In the following pages I describe how best to identify an accountant.

How To Find The Accountant That's Right For You

Most accountants will say they're 'proactive' or 'customer-focused', but there's no rule book to help business owners know what those words really mean. That leads to muddled expectations and often disappointment when you don't get the service you wanted.

You can be sure of what to expect from an AVN accountant. They can access a quality assurance system with an independently accredited set of standards. It's called AVN*Excellence* and it's a kind of ISO9000 for accountancy firms. So when a firm has AVN*Excellence* accreditation you can be sure that the promises they make are genuine.

Over 100 standards make up AVN*Excellence* and there are three levels of accreditation.

This is a brief description of each level and what it means for you. It's important to understand that all accountancy firms are capable of delivering on the descriptions below. These firms have demonstrated that they consistently offer and deliver these services to **all of their clients**.

As these are incremental stages, each level includes all of the benefits of the previous stage.

AVN*Excellence* 4 Star Accredited Firms – Consistently High Standards In Practice

These firms have transformed their practice in a truly proactive business, making the 22 things to expect from your accountant their minimum service. They use a systematic approach in everything they do from pricing their services (as opposed to give a ball park figure) to delivering on their promises. They've developed a fully involved team culture that's committed to delivering outstanding customer service.

What This Means For You

This means that nothing is left to chance when it comes to dealing with your affairs, even if a member of the team within the practice is sick. Your AVN accountant will take the time to meet with you more than once throughout the year and produce recommendations for your business.

AVN*Excellence* 5 Star Accredited Firms – Changing The Numbers That Matter

These firms have made the decision to only act for forward thinking clients who want to grow their business. They consistently offer and deliver the full nine step Performance Measurement and Improvement system with every business client. In addition they regularly run seminars for clients and prospects bringing insightful learning to their business community.

What This Means For You

If you're serious about changing the numbers in your business for the better, learning how to grow your business and networking with other businesses in your area then this level of AVN*Excellence* or higher is right for you.

AVN*Excellence* 6 Star Accredited Firms – Specialising In Business Growth

This is the pinnacle of excellence. Firms with the six star accreditation will take you on a transformational journey which makes your dreams a reality and gives you the time to do all the things you'd like to do when you're not working on your business. They help you transform your business into one that's profitable and enjoyable and isn't causing you stress. They help you get there at the pace you're most comfortable with and everything they offer comes with a guarantee that means if you're not 100% delighted you don't pay a penny.

All the benefits with absolutely no risk to you. Your personal and business aspirations will be clearly explored and understood. A business growth programme tailored to make your dreams happen will be offered to you completely risk free. Your AVN accountant will help you every step of the way.

In addition, some AVN accountants have not yet achieved AVN*Excellence* accreditation. They have, however, pledged their commitment to delivering high value to their clients. From complete transparency in pricing their services, to taking the time to spot opportunities for their clients and make recommendations in the areas of either personal wealth, business results, tax exposure or the value of the business, they will work with you to create action plans for those areas.

What This Means For You

It means that you'll have total clarity on what to expect from your accountant from the very first meeting. They'll work with you to establish your exact business needs and give you a calculated fixed price based on that. It means that the meetings you attend with your accountant will be a valuable use of your time and you'll come away with actions that will make your business stronger and more profitable – rather than merely discussing a set of accounts that reflect a period of time no longer relevant to you.

Directory of
AVN Accountants

The following accountants are listed according to their AVN *Excellence* accreditation. Each gives a brief synopsis of their firm and their location, who they prefer to work with and what really sets them apart so that you can decide which of the many accountants listed you'd prefer to have a conversation with.

The accountants are presented firstly by AVN*Excellence* accreditation; six star accredited firms first and then by their county and town so that you can, if you prefer, look for accountants near to you.

If you want to discuss your situation with an accountant and are still not sure who from this book to approach, I've given, in the following chapter, an alternative suggestion to finding an AVN Accountant to have a no obligation chat with.

businessVision

AVN*Excellence* 6 Star Accredited
Plymouth, Devon
Email Marc Lawson **marc@marclawson.co.uk**
Phone **01752 752210**
Website **www.bvisionaccountants.co.uk**

About Our Practice

---

businessVision are a Plymouth based firm of Chartered Accountants specialising in helping small and medium sized business owners achieve more but work less.

We focus on actively growing a business, not just reporting on its performance. Our passion, engagement and experience shine through in all client projects. We provide essential, valuable, strategic advice as standard as well as ahead of major decisions. To quote one satisfied client, *"a 35% increase in sales and over 100% increase in profit speak for themselves."*

We foster a lasting relationship with our clients and receive much of our new business through referrals from them. This relationship is founded on honesty, integrity and a genuine commitment to a client's business future.

We specialise in business growth and have provided over 130 growth training seminars to local businesses.

Our clients experience total peace of mind. All fees are fixed (no surprises!). They also receive a comprehensive guarantee that says if they don't feel we have delivered value they can pay whatever they want (even nothing). All clients have prompt delivery of bookkeeping, accounts and tax returns based on timetables discussed and agreed upon.

Why We Are Different

- Proactive advice saving tax and focusing on providing quantified value far higher than the fees
- Accounts prepared to an agreed timetable and delivered in 20 days
- Tax returns delivered in 14 days
- Unlimited emails, phone calls and meetings for a fixed monthly fee; clients never feel like the clock is ticking
- Free access to our online Business Growth System, the best step-by-step sales and marketing programme for small businesses in the UK
- A monthly sales and marketing newsletter packed with helpful tips and advice
- Profit growth and wealth growth meetings as standard

Who We Love To Work With

As specialists in business growth our ideal client should be ambitious and have a desire to grow.

For this reason we do not usually take on one-person businesses unless they have ambitions to grow beyond that in the near future. We are always happy to provide such businesses with free advice and recommendations to suitable accountants in the area. We usually act for businesses with a turnover between £100,000 and £5 million.

A particular specialism is that of businesses providing tradesmen and materials to customers (plumbers, electricians, shop fitters, roofers etc.) and we have had substantial success in helping this type of business increase sales and profit.

Generally our clients will be located in an area with a PL post-code.

An exception to the above is another specialism – personal service companies (such as in the IT industry) where we can usually supply a prompt efficient tax based service to any company based in the UK.

Ideally all clients are looking for value provided within the framework of fixed monthly fees and for an accountant who goes far beyond the provision of just accounts and one meeting a year.

Here's A Short Testimonial

"This is just a quick note to thank you very much for all the advice over the last few years. Although I was initially sceptical about the impact that this could have, the latest accounts prove that all the hard work combined with your advice is paying off. A 35% increase in sales and over 100% increase in profit speak for themselves. What has been particularly helpful has been the regular information coming through from the Business Builder Forum, which as you will know I have spent a lot of time implementing, and am pleased to say that this is now paying off dramatically. " –Toby Short

A Case Study That Demonstrates The Value We Deliver

A little over 12 months ago we started the One Page Plan process with a client of ours. The client had been a normal compliance client for many years and even though the business results were solid, both of the husband and wife directors felt that the business could do more, and both also wanted to take more of a back seat.

Our process began by analysing the existing figures using Success Driver Mapping. This indicated that their business earned money in two ways. Firstly, they brought materials and added on a mark-up when selling them to customers. Secondly, they provided technicians to do work who were charged out at an hourly rate. The Success Driver Mapping process indicated that there was a black hole in their figures. By taking realistic numbers for productivity, time off for sickness and holiday etc. we were able to show that (applying their target hourly rate for the number of technicians and the mark up on the amount of materials brought in the previous year) the target sales figure they should have achieved was substantially in excess of the figures they did actually achieve in their accounts. This gave us, and them, some confidence that analysing these figures in more detail would produce favourable results and would therefore justify the investment in the work.

Having signed the client up to the One Page Plan process we then completed a detailed yearly cash flow and profit forecast using the KPIs (Key Performance Indicators) mentioned in the Success Driver Mapping as part of the calculations.

The targets set out in the forecast were deliberately pushing the business to move somewhere quite dramatic rather than just going for the normal 3% or 5% increases. Included in the KPIs for the One Page Plan were the number of hours that the two directors were planning on working within the business.

In order to obtain accurate financial figures each month we set up Xero bookkeeping software for the client, and although they completed most of the bookkeeping work we were able to review this at the end of each month before pulling the figures into our own KPI software, 'Fathom.' Monthly meetings were held, at which point the finalised monthly management accounts and the figures in Fathom were presented together with detailed One Page Plan reports. The meeting went through all of the target numbers that weren't yet on target (and in the beginning this was nearly all of them) with a view to discussing and advising on how those individual figures could be moved closer to target.

By the end of the financial year for which the One Page Plan had been carried out. many, but not all, of the KPIs had reached target levels on a consistent basis. As a direct consequence of this sales had risen 13.8% (and this was in a business that had been trading for many years at the same level). More importantly, operating profit rose by 19.5% and profit after tax and dividends (dividends having increased by some £12,000) rose by a staggering 260%. The profit figures included the cost of doing the One Page Plan.

Now that the first year of the One Page Plan has ended we've been instructed to continue, with further increases in targets for the next year. The main difference being that both Directors have now effectively taken a back seat from the business and allowed a new Managing Director to move up through the ranks and continue in this process without their involvement. The Directors' only involvement in the business will be that they will be kept informed of any non-attendance at One Page Plans and will obviously receive summary figures at the end of each quarter. The Directors will continue to take the same level of dividends that they always have, and have ensured that the Managing Director, stepping into what was previously their role, will be on a bonus based on success results from the second year's One Page Plan.

MDH

AVN*Excellence* 6 Star Accredited
Croydon, Greater London
Email Michael Hemme **info@mdh.me.uk**
Phone **0208 647 0297**
Website **www.mdh.me.uk**

About Our Practice

A powerful business growth service to help you accelerate your business and achieve your personal vision by inspiring decisive action.

Sometimes it can be lonely being a business owner. Especially on those occasions when you have to take a leap of faith… a step forward into the unknown. Having someone by your side at those crucial times is invaluable – someone to give you the numbers, the systems, the possibilities and the belief to guide you. That's where, with proven financial expertise, plus the drive and passion to help you to achieve your life/business best, we can help.

Our fixed fee service is designed to help you focus and keep you on track with key processes in place; to keep you accountable and motivated. Carefully focused action is what we're built on – ours and yours. We know your time is precious, so we'll tell you which actions you need to start with for the biggest impact.

Accountancy And Business Growth Services

- Yes, we have the accreditations you'd expect from a regulated business
- Yes, we have the experience
- Yes, we have proven accountancy success
- We also offer you something more – a desire to go the extra mile, to help you achieve the success to make you happy

Why We Are Different

What we're about can be summed up in few words: we're all about you. About you having a vision and goal that we can help you drive towards as you build a better business. We can help you achieve the personal success you want.

Our team's skill sets, enthusiasm and drive provide you with an approach that goes above and beyond what you might expect from your accountant, giving you the practical support you need to succeed.

Sometimes it's nice to ask a trusted advisor 'What would you do?' Well, ask away. We don't sit on the fence – we don't shy away from difficult questions and brave decisions.

Who We Love To Work With

Are you getting what you want out of life? Or just more work than you bargained for – without the rewards you've dreamed of?
If, like so many business owners, your answer is 'no', my team

and I are here to help – to be by your side on the road to greater business success. We'll cut through the seeming 'madness' of it all and put you back in control. We'll help you clarify what you want. We'll help you examine the numbers, systemise your business and work towards the success that you've imagined for so long.

Our service isn't just for companies who have nearly 'made it'. If your business has more potential, but you don't know where to start, we can help with goal setting, forecasting and so much more in a practical, ready-to-go toolbox.

Or perhaps you're ready to shoot for the stars – we want to support you by helping you extract maximum value at every stage. We'll dedicate time and resource to supporting you to grow your business while maintaining stability. It's a high quality strategic planning and implementation support package to take you from where you are now to where you want to be. If your business is within 20 miles of Croydon call us today on 020 8647 0297.

Here's A Short Testimonial

"Working with MDH has helped us create a very healthy cash flow and account balance. This enables us to grow and invest in people, equipment and plant, if and when needed. There's nothing we can't do – having a good accountant gives us that freedom.

Michael is someone who knows our business, which is very important. He recommended taking on an apprentice accountant, which I've done. In fact, having MDH on board has changed an awful lot of things. Michael's always there in the background. At the end of the day, it comes down to a personal service."
–Chris Jennings, Director, GCSC (SW) Ltd

"He bends over backwards to make sure your needs are met."

The Background: Saving Money From The Start

Braving all market conditions in the depths of the recession in 2011, Alex Clarkson-Tooze set up Clarendons Property Consultants to deal with homes for sale and to rent throughout Surrey and West Sussex. Using a wealth of knowledge and experience, he had a vision of providing total property services in one place – with customer service excellence at its heart.

In 2010, with this high quality offering already in mind, Alex had started to piece everything together to create the first class support he knew would help him achieve it. One of the pieces in this jigsaw was having the right accountant. Alex said, *"I didn't know what I needed, I just knew that I needed one."* So he took advice from people in the know.

The Solution: A Different Approach

Four accountants were recommended to him by a major bank. The first three quoted Alex for a complete service – with four figure sums. But Michael Hemme at MDH, having asked some key questions about the kind of service Alex was looking for, took a different approach. He suggested training Alex up to do a lot of the accounts himself – which would cost a lot less money – and was also a solution that suited Alex perfectly. Alex said that Michael definitely saved him money through this – *"rather than trying to start me off on something I didn't need." It also showed him how transparent Michael was in the solutions he provided.*

"The service has evolved to meet our needs."

Alex has been working with Michael and his team at MDH ever since. He has always found their support to be *"responsive and flexible."* He said, *"Michael did something within the hour once because he knew I needed it."* As well as the ongoing training, MDH also delivers any additional accounts services required for Clarendons Property Consultants to remain compliant. With his excellent network, Michael helps Alex find other high quality professionals, which has saved him time and hassle too.

"We look at things from a different perspective."

MDH offers a service with another difference too – Michael works with Alex to give support on developing the business. Alex said, *"We meet twice a year and it's just helpful to speak to someone who isn't involved."* He added, *"He's gone through everything I have, shared experience and given me advice."*

The tangible benefits of this development work include Michael analysing what has already been done, providing constructive feedback on growth plans for the way forward and even, said Alex *"sometimes holding me back and putting things in perspective… putting systems in place."* He added, *"He always encourages you."* However, Michael isn't afraid to challenge ideas where appropriate too – an approach that Alex welcomes.

The Result: Supporting A Developing Company At Every Stage

From a standing start in 2011, Clarendons Property Consultants has grown every year, with MDH supporting it all the way – both through its responsive approach to accountancy and its business growth services.

Clarendons Property Consultants is on target for a turnover of £350,000 in the next financial year. The company is absolutely committed to first class results paired with fantastic customer service. So it is perhaps no surprise that Alex appreciates the high standards of service Michael offers. *"He bends over backwards to make sure your needs are met."*

Are you looking for an accounting solution, or support for accelerated business growth? Talk to Michael at MDH without obligation and he will make a recommendation tailored for you.

Blue Rocket Accounting

AVN*Excellence* 6 Star Accredited
Dartford, Kent
Email Julie Angell **julie@bluerocketaccounting.com**
Phone **01322 555442**
Website **www.bluerocketaccounting.com**

About Our Practice

Tax returns and bookkeeping are a given. You can go to any accountants for that. Where Blue Rocket differs is the proactive advice, support and planning the team offers to their clients. They know the importance of having someone there to ask questions, keeping clients going when they need a bit of encouragement, and celebrating their successes with them. They like to think of themselves as an accounting version of a personal trainer.

If you had to sum up what they're all about in one sentence, it's this:

Putting honest, professional and committed business owners firmly on course to reach their goals with a tailored programme of accounting support that gives them the critical information they need to build the business they always wanted.

True to their name, Blue Rocket will help business owners soar into space and reach the stars, and they'll be there with them for the journey.

Why We Are Different

We don't just provide accountancy services. Our clients benefit from a range of business support experts (not just us!) which we make available to them free of charge. Together with our trusted experts we run regular seminars and workshops giving practical hints and tips to help entrepreneurs run their businesses effectively and profitably, helping them to get the life and the business they want.

We also help them to grow their businesses by running networking events over a bite to eat and drink, or racing cars around a Scalextric track!

Who We Love To Work With

We work with clients at all stages of their business journey, whether they are a start-up, or a successful business owner who has been established for many years. The thing that they all have in common is their passion – to grow and succeed in their business. They are looking for support, not just a firm of accountants to speak to once a year when they need their accounts doing.

We work best with our clients when we are part of their team, so we need to understand, and be involved with their business goals, and we'll do everything we can to help them achieve them.

We have packages available for start-up businesses to get them off the ground and support them through their first two years, a business that has been operating for a few years, but wants to take their business to the next level, and for those business owners who want to reach the stars.

We don't mind where you are based, but we do love our clients to pop in for a cup of tea, a biscuit, or if they want to let off some steam with our Scalextric track that we have in the basement!

Here's A Short Testimonial

"Blue Rocket Accounting is a highly professional but equally friendly company who puts our business needs at the heart of what they do. Their processes and procedures are well thought out with the customer in mind at every turn and everything is included in a fixed price – you don't have to worry about asking a question and wondering how much they are adding to your bill. They stick to their schedule and you know you won't have to wait weeks to get the work done. We would highly recommend them and are very pleased we made the leap to Blue Rocket." –Sarah Redpath, Leisure King Ltd

A Case Study That Demonstrates The Value We Deliver

The Rouge Partnership Limited is an event management specialist, and an established business which has operated successfully for many years. Attending their pre-year end planning meeting with Blue Rocket, the Directors were looking forward to sharing record profits with the team. Armed with their management accounts, they broke the good news. However, what they didn't realise was that their great profits had left them with a staggering tax bill of £217,175! Not only that, but the company were paying an effective tax rate of 29.75% when large companies only pay 28%. Clearly worried about their tax liability, they said *"The thought of paying that amount of tax was making us feel physically sick"*, and so Blue Rocket quickly got to work.

The team established the true situation through structured tax planning questions, and a solution was found.

Simple, but effective tax planning reduced the overall tax rate Rouge paid to a more manageable and realistic 21% – a saving of over 8%. In addition, their tax bill was significantly reduced, saving Rouge a whopping £137,993.

The team said of the result, *"Keeping in regular contact with you guys* (Blue Rocket) *has proved to be one of the best business decisions we ever made."*

Northern Accountants Ltd

....

AVN*Excellence* 6 Star Accredited
Leeds, West Yorkshire
Email Phil Ellerby **8steps@northernaccountants.co.uk**
Phone **0113 2189552**
Website **www.northernaccountants.co.uk**

About Our Practice
....

Northern Accountants help people get the most out of their business and to provide a better life for themselves today, whilst planning for tomorrow. Building a business that allows them to go on holiday when they want to, fund their children through university and, comfortably plan for a happy retirement.

Why We Do What We Do...
....

We believe in Lifetime Financial Responsibility, the ability to plan, and be able to fund personal financial milestones.
Borne out of experience from our own lives and from growing our own successful and profitable business, we are passionate about the difference we make. We want to help people plan their business but ultimately their personal growth.

We do this through a number of key services:

1. The Numbers – as a way to grow the business
2. Doo Marketing – as a way to deliver that planned growth
3. TaxSmart – ways to protect the business
4. Cloud Accounting – ways to manage, finance and understand the business

Adding value to what is expected as typical accountants, our compliance services include:

-   Bookkeeping
-   Payroll
-   VAT
-   CIS
-   Self-assessments

Why We Are Different

We have been in our clients shoes. With first-hand experience of what you are going through, we know what it takes. We have been bust but took the decision early to take 'The Numbers' journey and there is no bigger success story than ours.

Taking a whole life view, we know what happens in business affects our personal lives. We give our clients the support, the tools and the systems to build successful, profitable businesses.

Leading by example, we work with our clients to create a business which will ensure a financially secure lifestyle for them and their loved ones.

You are an all-round forward thinking business person with aspirations for growth, keen to get to the next level but not sure how. Possibly frustrated, alone, ready to come off the tools, but feeling trapped with work issues and personal pressures. You want to work on the business rather than in it.

You have arrived at a stage where you know you want more, for you and your loved ones, tired of working long hours, watching the pennies, living day by day, taking work and stress levels home with you.

You may have a young family and are local to Leeds, Wakefield, West Yorkshire. You are hungry for success and open to invest in your business. You are ready to change, listen and learn.
Our clients range from early 30s – 40s, a mix of male and females. They need a plan and are willing to take steps to ensure the next level is within reach – nice car, nice house, holidays when they want them, time for their families with a business that supports their lifestyle.

This is what we do best as this relates to our circumstances too. We want to help you Do Less Work and Earn More Money with a financial security for a lifetime.

Here's A Short Testimonial

"Working with Northern Accountants has not only saved me money, it has made me money as they have generated me far more money

than I have paid them. We were in a completely different place when we first started. They helped us with cash flow, pricing, the business structure and much needed office support. We started on 'The Numbers programme' straight away. I now know where every penny of my money goes to in the business and this has made a massive difference; mainly the improvement it made to our personal lives and what we could give to our families." –Gavin Esberger GME Painting Contractor

---

A Case Study That Demonstrates The Value We Deliver
....

GME Painting Contractors – Gavin Esberger & Matthew Edwards

A small commercial painting contractor, mainly serving the construction industry, based in Leeds but working nationwide. Started trading in 2007 with a van, some brushes and four weeks of confirmed work. Prior to meeting Northern Accountants they had a turnover of £300k and a Net Profit of £15k (Net Profit Margin 5%).

Situation
....

With poor cash flow, NP margin, limited personal income, poor, out of date accounting information and a number of bad clients they were totally disillusioned with everything. Their day to day commitments meant they had no time to plan so they lacked structure and a vision for the company. At the time they were working from Matthew's garage, surrounded by stock and attending meetings smelling of paint. They were trying to win work they had been used to when they were employed by one of

Yorkshire's biggest painting and decorating companies.

It was clear from meeting the guys at our Business Builder session using the SSTW software, that there was huge potential in both the business and the Directors. They simply lacked clarity of vision and solid structured advice on how to get to their end goal. Their needs perfectly suited our 'Numbers' programme, an adapted version of the AVN PMI system. We started by completing their Personal Balance Sheet which really opened the Directors' eyes, with both quickly realising that the company was not delivering, nor had it delivered, what they had expected it to do when they formed in 2007. From the PBS we generated their personal goals which looked at their incomes, personal wealth, number of hours worked, holidays, work life balance, retirement plans and many other things. We then mapped their business goals to deliver their personal goals.

One of the key personal goals for Gavin was to buy a new, bigger house so he and his wife Nikki could start a family. We met with our IFA to understand the earnings Gavin and Nikki would need to have to secure sufficient lending to move into their dream home and start their family. We tweaked the business goals to deliver this earning level for both Directors. We then extended the business goals to create the company's first set of forecasts and corresponding budgets. This was the first time the Directors had a true vision of what the company needed to do to achieve their personal goals. We, as a firm, helped the company by seconding a member of staff to work with them on a full time interim basis.

We helped recruit Sasha, their Office Manager, and a vital cog in the GME machine.

We revisited the PBS and Personal Goals. This again led to business goals, forecasts and budgets being produced for 2014. Now the accounting information was up to date and accurate, we could produce monthly management information. This information was transformed and mapped into a One Page Plan which was measured monthly and discussed at monthly BoardView meetings. These meetings showed a huge shift was required to move out of construction and into repaints where the margins are better, payment terms are better and there is far less exposure to application disputes.

While reshaping the client's offering, things started moving quickly in Gavin's personal life. Gavin and his wife embarked on the adoption process in 2012. With the success of 2013, Gavin was able to buy the house they needed and later that year they became the proud parents of baby George.

2014 saw the Directors wanting to take the business into new trading industries yet it was apparent that their image did not match their intentions. We helped them create a strategic marketing plan though our marketing company. It has seen the business develop a new website, improve their brand consistency, develop strong marketing collateral and enhance their social media presence. This was factored into the forecasts and budgets for 2015. By the end of Q1, Matthew was no longer on the tools and was running the business operationally in its entirety.

We advised GME to raise prices by 10% to start to improve the margins under which the business operated. This resulted in a loss of no clients, with all accepting the price increase without question or comment. This simply increased profitability. We helped the company restructure its internal accounts department. Implementing regular, timely and accurate management information which meant the company could make decisions on fact rather than a gut feeling, thereby increasing profitability by capitalising on opportunity and addressing costly errors. By setting up processes and systems that managed the company's cash flow on a daily basis they were able to plan future projects more accurately, meaning they could take on larger, more profitable jobs. We assessed the company's client base and produced an ideal client profile, embarking on a project of 'sacking' bad clients, allowing them to focus on better jobs and clients.

GME are overwhelmed with the success of the business. The change in management style and proper use of 'The Numbers' has revolutionised the results of the company. From a small company, they are now recognised as being one of the top three painting and decorating companies in Yorkshire. Their cash flow is much improved, their processes work and are adhered to and they have a far better idea of the clients they want. They know which jobs to go for, they are able to cost jobs better and they plan resource and material more efficiently.

GME's future is much clearer. The Directors have a vision for the company and know exactly where they want to go and what the business will do for them in retirement, for their benefit, that of their employees and more importantly their families.

AA Accountants

AVN*Excellence* 5 Star Accredited
Peterborough, Cambridgeshire
Email **Shahzad Nawaz shaz@aa-accountants.co.uk**
Phone **01733 785997**
Website **www.aa-accountants.co.uk**

About Our Practice

One word sums us up – 'excellence.' Our 5 star AVN*Excellence* accreditation is just one example of our commitment to excel in everything we do.

We are a small, highly-qualified team. Our skills are sought after by clients all over the country.

Our ambitious and enthusiastic clients want more than 'mainstream' accountancy. We specialise in business growth, tax reduction and mitigation, and wealth management, working closely with sought-after experts in specialised areas of accountancy and taxation.

It's not a case of 'one strategy fits all.' We listen to our clients and as a consequence provide an outstanding bespoke service. Client care and contact underpin all our systems and processes. Our Gold standard in Investors in People demonstrates the value we place in our team.

Meeting with clients twice a year is an absolute minimum. However, we provide quarterly management meetings, proactive calls and meetings, as well as specialist advice. Our clients come to us BEFORE making major decisions, as they see immense value in our expertise. It's a great opportunity to look at tax planning and mitigation, including strategies that can only be put in place before the event, not after!

Why We Are Different

We are not just number-crunchers, producing historic accounts for the benefit of statutory bodies!
Our tried, tested, proven cutting-edge approach really works.
For concrete proof please visit
www.aa-accountants.co.uk/case-studies
We analyse your information, benchmark it against your industry and come up with strategies to maximise your turnover and profit whilst minimising your costs and tax. We support you in achieving your maximum potential.
We offer a fixed fee with no surprise bills, ever! And if we can't carry out the work to your reasonable satisfaction – we offer a 100% money-back guarantee!

Who We Love To Work With

Our ideal clients are ambitious and determined to become increasingly more successful. They recognise they need external advice and support in order to achieve this.

Our ideal client avatar:

- Business owners seriously committed to growing their business
- Annual turnover in excess of £1m
- Typically between 1 – 5 business owners
- Able to accept the positive benefit of a solid and modern business infrastructure
- Consider their accountant to be an investment

Some of your challenges may be:
- Lack of sales – we help you formulate an expansive sales and marketing process in order to increase sales
- Lack of profits – by improving your pricing, customer-retention and reducing overheads we will assist you in increasing your profits
- Lack of tax-planning – we work with you to devise a strategy to manage and reduce tax liabilities as well as review advanced tax planning and tax allowances
- Lack of accountability – we act as a sounding board to explore key challenges, issues and ideas, and monitor how well you achieve your aims
- Poor accounting systems – we offer advice and training by using the latest Cloud-based technology and demonstrate how it can improve efficiency

Here's A Short Testimonial

"From the word go we were extremely impressed with how quickly aa Chartered Accountants understood where we were going, what we wanted and needed. Shaz formulated a brilliant business plan, securing for us a £40 million funding offer. He managed

and negotiated the deal at every level. We couldn't have got there without him. It's life-changing. Stuff of dreams! He thinks outside the box which is great. He looks for a solution, constantly. I've never had, regardless of the level or amount of money I've paid, the kind of service and support they offer. It's pretty unique." –Martin Walker, XL Limited

---

A Case Study That Demonstrates The Value We Deliver

£22k of tax saved in year one and £41k in year two comes in as a handy tool for East Anglian Resources!

East Anglian Resources was formed in 2009 by patriarch, James Tribe. The company's growth was mercurial and James enlisted the help of his family to support him. Trust is a big thing with James. It was only logical he would turn to those he trusted most, his family, to assist him.

James is proud of the business he has built. He is not afraid of hard work or getting his hands dirty, he understands his business from the ground up and his family have inherited a similar work ethic. The initial success of this wood recycling business was brilliant, but the owners found themselves feeling isolated and exposed to risk. They knew they needed someone to provide independent and objective support and advice. This was critical in order to create sustainable growth for their business and its long term future.

James is an astute businessman. While he loves working with his close family and welcomes the trust he has in them, he also understands the value of sound investment, not only in plant and machinery, but also in people and advisors. He wanted to work with people who genuinely had his best interests at heart.

He was quick to realise that they had outgrown their current accountants and needed to work with someone who could advise them on how to systemise their business and make it more efficient. He wanted to work with people who had knowledge and expertise in business growth and tax mitigation, and who would work with him to ensure he paid the minimum legal tax on his profits.

James had a clear idea of what success meant and it wasn't just about the money in the bank. Success meant having a profitable business that continued to run efficiently in his absence. It meant having time to relax and spend with his family without worrying about things going wrong.

He needed someone who could push him and keep him focused on the important issues. James wanted someone who would work with him to bring his dreams to fruition.

The three main business concerns:
- How to control the growth in a profitable manner
- How to ensure they were maximising all tax reliefs and allowances in order to pay the least amount of tax
- To find an entrepreneurial accountant who could provide support beyond accountancy and tax to support James' grand plans

Following an introduction by their bank manager, James and Bobby instantly connected with Shaz and the team. The team were willing to go that extra mile to ensure a smooth change over from their previous accountants, minimising the contact and headache for James and Bobby by making time for them when they needed it.

By spending time with aa Chartered Accountants team, James was able to build up great rapport and they quickly became his trusted advisors. He felt completely at ease approaching them in advance of all decisions and welcomed their advice and perspective. James fully understood that tax planning is something which needs to be done in advance rather than retrospectively.

Shaz initially revealed how the business could further grow and maximise profit, which was exactly what James wanted.

The first thing James wanted was his previous year's accounts completed within two weeks. aa Chartered Accountants managed this with ease. At the year-end accounts meeting James was told about the £22k tax savings – this was an added bonus for the family!

The Right Results

- Within three months James moved the book-keeping and management accounts to aa Chartered Accountants
- More time was created for the family to focus on growing the business
- Loans to fund the purchase of equipment were secured through the help of aa Chartered Accountants
- James engaged Shaz and the team as their trusted advisors and business mentors

"aa Chartered Accountants introduced the business to Xero Cloud Accounting, which has seen a major improvement in record keeping and accounting systems. They have supported us with training and have shown us how to use the system efficiently.

The benefit of Cloud accounting is that we have real time information that shows us quickly and accurately where we are at any given moment in time.

Furthermore management information allows us to make better informed key decisions based on our circumstances. Regular meetings with aa Chartered Accountants to discuss our numbers has allowed us to plan the growth of our business, improve cash flow and better manage our liabilities.

In addition, we are able to generate reports on crucial key performance indicators (KPIs) that enable us to track the key numbers in our business, highlighting segments which are profitable and those that need further investigation in order to improve results."

James feels confident he can now grow the company to ten times its size with the support of aa Chartered Accountants.

The company has seen sales grow by 166% in one year alone and profits have grown by 218%. James is now looking to buy his own premises to support future growth.

Another area where aa Chartered Accountants provided help and support was with negotiating a major new contract. Their expertise was invaluable and refreshing.

Client Comment

Bobby Tribe said *"Nothing is too much trouble, they are always willing to go that extra mile for us. There is no such thing as 9 – 5 with them. They understand the need to be there for us when we need them."*

James Tribe said *"Working with aa Chartered Accountants has given me the confidence to grow my business even more. They get on with the financial and tax work so I can focus on managing my business.*

Shaz is an excellent business growth expert. He has opened my eyes to what I can achieve and he's going to help me get there too! In year one they saved me £22k in tax followed by £41k in the next year. No one has ever done that for me before. I'm so glad I'm working with Shaz and his team – they are a great support to me and my family.

If you get the chance to work with Shaz – grab it! He doesn't work with everybody and anybody."

Jonathan Vowles

CHARTERED ACCOUNTANTS

Jonathan Vowles Chartered Accountants

AVN Accountant
Cranfield, Bedfordshire
Email Jonathan Vowles **jonathan@vowles.co.uk**
Phone **01234 752566**
Website **www.jvca.co.uk**

About Our Practice

JVCA... chartered accountants, chartered tax accountants, business advisors and tax specialists.

Do you deserve more from your accountant? Maybe it is time to get the business advisors you need, as well as the account-ants and tax advisors you deserve. Okay, so every business has got an accountant, but there are accountants and then there is JVCA!

We do a lot more than just number crunching! We are more like bean roasters than bean counters, providing the warm glow of being looked after by a professional, full service firm of advisors.

We provide solutions – both the basics, to sort your day-to-day accounting needs, and the really useful proactive or planning services that can make a huge difference to you and your business.

Who We Love To Work With

Our ideal client is someone who wants to improve and get more from their business – and has employees, so isn't just a 'one man band'. Normally this means a business with more than £500,000 in sales but we have also helped start-up businesses grow and succeed. We love using our tax knowledge to make a difference and can deliver a range of things to help you pay less tax, whether you have £100k profits or £10m in profits! Of course, if your profits aren't that big yet, then you can benefit from our profit improvement advice.

Whilst modern technology means distance really isn't an issue, the majority of our clients are located less than 75 minutes commute from our offices in Cranfield.

Why We Are Different

Very few things in business are unique, other than people, of course. However, we are not the same as any old firm of accountants! The things we do are not commonly found. Our tax planning advice is world class, our management accounting will provide you with fantastic insights and understanding of your business and our business advice has made a positive difference to many of our clients. Really you need to meet us to talk through the ways in which we can help you and your business thrive to understand why JVCA is a cut above the average.

Starfish Accounting

AVN Accountant
Littlewick Green, Berkshire
Email Georgi Rollings **georgi@starfishaccounting.co.uk**
Phone **01628 828855**
Website **www.starfishaccounting.co.uk**

About Our Practice

Founded in 2010 by Georgina Rollings (Georgi), Starfish Accounting is all about approachable, friendly, non-stuffy advice and support for growing businesses. We are a small firm of Chartered Accountants that pride ourselves on being a little bit different. We are passionate about the use of technology to drive better business performance. Working with you in partnership we help to develop business growth strategies instead of just looking in the rear view mirror.

We strongly believe that technology is there to make your life easier. By implementing a combination of leading cloud software solutions including Xero (Starfish Accounting is proud to be a Xero gold champion partner) and Receipt Bank we can move you to real time availability of easy to understand financial information. This gives you the power to make the right business decisions at the right time to achieve significant improvements in both profit levels and cash flow.

Who We Love To Work With

With a particular focus on women in business (but we do welcome and work well with male business owners too), Starfish Accounting is made up chiefly of mums. This keeps the team grounded and in the real world, and we understand the extra challenges created by having to juggle business and family. At the last count around a third of our clients are male. But our belief, rightly or wrongly, is that it can be harder for women in business to get the support that they need, and we want to fill some of that gap.

We work with small businesses ranging from start-ups at the very start of their business journey through to established companies with turnover of up to £2 million and beyond. Working with business owners who are motivated and ambitious to achieve the best for their businesses and their families means that we love what we do. We take the extra time to nurture our clients and help them to identify the next steps for growth.

The majority of our clients are based in the Thames Valley in Maidenhead, Twyford, Reading and surrounding areas, however we have clients located across the UK.

Why We Are Different

We provide accounting, tax and bookkeeping services, together with business advice and support, which ensures compliance and helps to drive profitability. We all find it incredibly satisfying to help to create order from chaos. We also strongly believe that a good accountant should save their clients more money than they cost. Why settle for an accountant that just prepares your accounts and tax returns when you can instead move forward to a different way of working with up to date accurate financial information?

Let us work with you to help you achieve the business you have always wanted.

Hallidays Group Limited

AVN Accountant
Stockport, Cheshire
Email Nigel Bennett **nigelb@hallidays.co.uk**
Phone **0161 476 8276**
Website **www.hallidays.co.uk**

About Our Practice

More than just accountants, Hallidays are a modern and innovative business that believes in growing and supporting our clients.

We work closely with SME's with specialist knowledge of academies, charities, solicitors, and credit unions. We help our clients by providing expert advice on business growth, tax planning, business planning and restructuring, wealth management, and of course all of your everyday compliance. At the early stages of our relationship, we'll work with you to establish your expectations to ensure we are all heading in the same direction.

Our membership with Russell Bedford gives you access to a worldwide network of professional service firms. Our connection with The Corporate Finance Network further enhances our capability to fully prepare and support you with raising finance, mergers and acquisitions, and with exit strategies.

For over 10 years, Hallidays' clients have voted personal service as one of the key things they love about us along with approachability and other areas such as speed of response, fixed fees, and most importantly helping to grow their businesses.

So, if you are a business or charity that wants to grow... please give us a call.

Who We Love To Work With

If you are an ambitious growing business that wants to work closely with a professional adviser to help you achieve your personal and business goals then please get in touch.

Why We Are Different

By taking a 360-degree view of you and your business, we will guide you through the challenging steps of growing. Our growth service is tailored towards an ambitious growing business that wants to work closely with a professional adviser to help them achieve their personal and business goals.

Here's A Short Testimonial

"We started out as two freelancers and the benefit of objective business experts and the camaraderie of the Business AM events has encouraged us to take the right actions. Hallidays' support and

insight, combined with the Business One Page Plan has enabled us to grow, achieve our goals and win an amazing award." –Stuart Bradley, Business Owner, Trust Brand Communications

"The action we have taken as a result of attending Hallidays' Business AM has been a catalyst for change and has enabled us to transform our business and achieve our goals." –Joe Pritchard, Director, Maggi Electronics Ltd

A Case Study That Demonstrates The Value We Deliver

Trust, a branding and digital agency started life working out of two premises. They needed to grow and put a plan in place which they did with the help of Hallidays and their Business One Page Plan.

The two directors needed to align their vision for the business and agree goals and targets to drive the business forward. They needed to identify the value they provide, rather than communicating the features of their service to their customers.

With Hallidays' support, Trust used our Kickstart questionnaire to develop their shared vision and goals. They now have a clear 'USP' and money-back guarantee proving clients with peace of mind.

Before

The team of two were working from separate premises which impacted on their personal life and day to day communication which ultimately could have a long term impact on client service.

After

Hallidays advised on and facilitated their move into one premises which improved communication and ultimately the day-to-day stress for the team.

Before

Trust recognised that pricing based on time was not the right way to grow their business. They needed to review their pricing model to one based on value and introduce ways of maximising their cash flow.

After

Hallidays worked with the Trust team to develop the right pricing module based on value and payment structure which improved their cash flow. Trust also benefited from attending Hallidays' Business AM event focusing on price and product position for maximum profit.

Before

Growing the business was an overwhelming challenge they needed to focus on. This impacted on the business systems and identifying KPI's to achieve the growth they wanted.

After

Working together their Business One Page Plan was produced. Now Hallidays meet quarterly with Trust to review their success and advise where action needs to be taken.

Outcome

From working out of two premises, Trust brought the business under one roof which improved their communication and speed of response.

By year 3 they were attending Hallidays Business AM growth sessions and their Business One Page Plan was in place which ensured they focused on what was important to the business. Using the Business One Page Plan as a monthly snapshot of everything that matters to the business ensures they focus on the actions that help grow the business.

They have now taken the next step in their growth strategy by hiring a new team member to focus on lead generation and business development.

What The Client Said

"We've been able to beat our previous year's turnover in 8 months. We put this down to measuring the things that matter on our BOPP. The icing on the cake was winning the Stockport Business Award for 'Business of the Year - up to £1 million'." –Stuart Bradley, Business Owner - Trust Brand Communications

Our clients experience total peace of mind. All fees are fixed (no surprises!). They also receive a comprehensive guarantee that says if they don't feel we have delivered value they can pay whatever they want (even nothing). All clients have prompt delivery of bookkeeping, accounts and tax returns based on timetables discussed and agreed upon.

McKellens

AVN Accountant
Stockport, Cheshire
Email Chris Booth **chris.booth@mck.co.uk**
Phone **0161 947 4888**
Website **www.mck.co.uk**

About Our Practice

Our aim is to help businesses become the most successful and enjoyable to run in the UK.

At McKellens we believe it should go without saying that your accountant will deliver all the basics accurately and on time, so we won't go on about that here. (If you do want details about our products and services you can find this and much more, on our website **www.mck.co.uk**). And, to be frank, accounts and tax returns are not much use if you're looking to move your business forward.

What's far more important is that we know exactly what you want from your business as owning, running and growing a business is simply a vehicle for you to achieve your personal goals and dreams. Once we understand that then we can work together and help you identify and put into practice what you need to do to get there.

We want your business to be successful and enjoyable. If you want that too, then let's work together to make it happen!

Why We Are Different

Why choose McKellens?
- Approachability
- Plain English
- You'll know the cost – no nasty surprises or unexpected bills
- Proactive business advice
- Always contactable
- Numbers that are useful
- Proactive tax advice
- Talking is free
- Real time accounting solutions
- Peace of mind
- The McKellens Business Accelerator – our monthly business learning environment designed to give you ideas and encouragement to grow your business
- One Page Plans – knowing how you are doing without having to do boring accounts
- Benchmarking – knowing how you are doing compared to others in your industry

Who We Love To Work With

Our ideal client is a business where the business owner wants the business to be successful and enjoyable. We cover all sectors/industries and all sizes of business from start-ups to multi million pound turnover businesses.

Where we can best help is with businesses who want and need a Virtual Finance Director. This is where we can play to our strengths whilst helping the business owner on their journey to achieve their personal goals and dreams.

We have clients all over the country and with the use of email, video calls and Cloud accounting solutions it really doesn't matter where our clients are. Having said that, we are based in South Manchester and so the majority of our clients are based in and around Greater Manchester, Cheshire and West Yorkshire.

We offer a special start-up service for new businesses which has proved so successful that businesses are four times more likely to get through the start-up phase with McKellens than by not being with us. Get in touch for further details.

JD & Co

AVN Accountant
Wrexham, Clwyd
Email **Tim Davies tim@johndavies.biz**
Phone **01978 263614**
Website **www.johndavies.biz**

About Our Practice

We aim to add value to privately owned, dynamic, hard-working businesses; businesses owned by people who live and breathe what they do.

We are highly experienced at managing our clients' compliance needs, but we will also give you real-time financial reporting and advice, so you know how your business is performing day-to-day, rather than a year down the track. You will get robust quality advice to help your business grow and prosper.

Our advice is practical and hands-on, based on real experience and hard data. We work in the real world, just like you do.

Why We Are Different

We will be an extension of your team and will constantly be

there to help you grow and prosper. We will not only provide general business advice, but will focus on detailed tax and strategic planning to help you succeed. We focus on the future not the past and work tirelessly to help you reach your goals whether financial or non-financial.

Who We Love To Work With

We work with SMEs who have enthusiasm and passion for what they do. We have helped clients grow from start-up to over £12 million in turnover, and then guided them through the successful sale of the business. We want to help businesses grow and prosper whilst having fun in doing so. We cover all industries and with our investment in technology can be your Virtual Finance Director wherever you are in the UK, or even overseas.

 **Dawn McLaughlin & Co**
Chartered Accountants

Dawn McLaughlin & Co

AVN Accountant
Londonderry, County Londonderry
Email Dawn McLaughlin **dawn@dawnmclaughlin.co.uk**
Phone **02871 370886**
Website **www.dawnmclaughlin.co.uk**

About Our Practice

Dawn McLaughlin & Co was established in 2005 by Dawn McLaughlin who qualified with a Big Four firm and has over 30 years of experience with SMEs. Dawn has been working with a number of family businesses throughout this time, providing high quality business focused mentoring, training and support. The award winning practice is located in Derry/Londonderry with clients throughout Northern Ireland. The client portfolio is diversified over a wide range of industry sectors.

At Dawn McLaughlin & Co, the services go beyond providing accounts and tax returns. They work with you, asking the right questions to set the path for you to achieve your financial goals. The quality of their individual client relationships is the key to their success. Since no two clients are alike, no two solutions are alike either. Their diversified professional experience, combined with advanced technology, enables them to provide dynamic business solutions to meet your needs and exceed your expectations. As a Sage Gold Partner they lead the way with Cloud accounting systems.

With Dawn McLaughlin & Co your interests always come first, giving you a trusted partner bringing big-picture perspective and the support you deserve.

Why We Are Different

Our passion is to help you grow your business, overcome obstacles, prosper and realise your dreams.

Setting us apart is the attention from the personal approach of our team. We are easy to talk to, easy to understand and easy to work with, returning calls promptly and meeting at your convenience. You gain a real connection yielding real value.

We look beyond the numbers to understand your world, finding new ways to help you improve your financial operations and results, keeping you on top of changes and ahead of trends. We connect you to resources through our wide network of professional and business contacts.

Who We Love To Work With

Our ideal clients have a vision for their business and the drive to move it forward. They understand their limitations and are prepared to engage the appropriate support and develop the necessary skills to succeed and grow. We get great satisfaction from working with owner managed businesses to relieve them of their compliance burden, provide peace of mind and free up their time to deal with more pressing tasks.

With regard to compliance we do not work with regulated sectors such as charities and solicitors, and we are not registered auditors. We have no limits on size or time in business, however we do have minimum fee structures and we have set payment terms.

We encourage all new starts to subscribe to our Easystart programme. We want to provide our clients with the best possible start for their business venture. New starts need to want to achieve success and be prepared to listen to our advice.

As a specialist area within the practice we work with and encourage female business owners as Dawn's passion is to inspire and empower women to succeed.

Our strategy as a Sage Gold Partner is to move all clients with manual records to Sage One getting them ready for HMRC's making tax digital policy.

dpaccounting

DP Accounting Ltd

AVN Accountant
Chesterfield, Derbyshire
Email David Potter **david@dpaccounting.co.uk**
Phone **01246 451133**
Website **www.dpaccounting.co.uk**

About Our Practice

Getting the financial support you need to run and grow your business.

Since 1995, DP Accounting 'Are more than just numbers.' We believe that work should deliver a lifestyle, not rob you of one. That is why our accountancy services and financial support are friendly and personal, tailored to helping you to run and grow your business.

Our belief is that your accountant should be in regular contact with you, not that elusive someone you only speak to once a year. We maintain that you should have all the key financial information for your business in a clear and concise format you can understand. At DP Accounting, we will work with you to build your business and help you to achieve your goals.

The practice has grown to provide a diverse range of specialist services to all forms and types of business.

Over the years we have come to realise that whilst there is still a need for traditional accountancy services, there is far more that can be done to help and support our customers.

Why We Are Different

A unique development programme for you to:
- Re-awaken the dream
- Get off the Treadmill
- Understand what you really want and make it happen

The journey starts with:
- Initial 1-2-1 coaching to establish your personal and business goals
- A personal communications and strengths analysis
- Motivations and needs analysis
- Eight monthly workshops
- Financial analysis including review tools
- One page business plan
- Support to keep you Inspired, focused, and on track
- Part of small business group providing sharing of challenges faced and working together to create innovative solutions

Who We Love To Work With

Primarily we are looking to work with private sector business owners in South Yorkshire and Derbyshire who have an established business with four or more employees, a turnover of £500,000+, who are not achieving the rewards and lifestyle they deserve.

They will see DP Accounting as a valuable member of their team helping them to achieve greater profitability, better employee involvement, improved work life balance and a real sense of purpose.

They will be committed to using computerised bookkeeping and Cloud accountancy software, together with implementing operational, customer, marketing and people systems

We want to work closely with our clients… therefore we must like them! So a pleasant personality is essential.

dekm
chartered
accountants

DEKM Limited

AVN Accountant
Derby, Derbyshire
Email Paul Bradley **paul.bradley@dekm.co.uk**
Phone **01332 293396**
Website **www.dekm.co.uk**

About Our Practice

A forward looking firm helping its clients achieve remarkable results from the provision of practical advice, which is monitored and updated at regular meeting with clients including the use of the Virtual Finance Director facility.

The firm fully embraces the use of Cloud technology to provide the maximum benefits for its clients and are a QuickBooks Gold ProAdvisor.

We offer a full range of services including accounting, audit, payroll, auto enrolment, VAT, cash flow, budgeting, incorporation, tax advice and planning.

Our team are dedicated to providing a fast efficient service to meet all your requirements.

We believe that looking forward is more important than looking back.

This enables us to offer practical advice which makes a real difference to your business.

Why We Are Different

A large number of business owners have difficulties moving from being self-employed where they do the work, to being a business owner where they make the decisions and let others do the work. In other words where they 'work on' the business rather than 'work in' the business. This is where our expert guidance and knowledge comes in to guide you through this process.

Who We Love To Work With

Our ideal client is one who embraces the same values as ourselves with a forward looking approach. The business will normally be a company, a partnership or a sole trader operating within 20 miles of our offices. The turnover will range from £100,000 to £20,000,000.

Being based in Derby we have considerable experience of engineering and manufacturing companies together with the associated design services, although we also deal with a vast range of business including retail, leisure, professional and transport.

With the use of the Internet, Cloud technology and Skype our area of operation is extended.

accountancyEdge

Earn more. Keep more. Enjoy it more.

Accountancy Edge

AVN Accountant
Bideford, Devon
Email James Hellyer **james@accountancy-edge.co.uk**
Phone **01237 421342**
Website **www.accountancy-edge.co.uk**

About Our Practice

James Hellyer qualified as a Chartered Accountant while working for KPMG, one of the Big Four, where he worked with blue chip clients. After returning to Devon to work with smaller businesses he was surprised to find that most small business accountants were only interested in completing end of year accounts and tax returns, and that despite claims to the contrary they had little interest in adding value to their clients' businesses. So, in 2010 James decided to set up his own accountancy practice to do things the way they should be done, in a way that helped business owners become more successful. He thought their accountants should give their businesses an advantage, an edge, and Accountancy Edge was born.

Accountancy Edge is based in Bideford, North Devon, and works with a range of owner managed businesses throughout Devon, Cornwall and Somerset (and sometimes beyond). As well as taking the stress out of a business owner's compliance obligations (basically their accounts and tax), it wants to work with them to help them take their business from where it is now to wherever they want to be.

Why We Are Different

Every year for each trading client, we review whether they are utilising the most tax efficient trading vehicle and make a clear recommendation to them about this. We will check you are on the best VAT scheme for your business. We will review how you remunerate yourself from your business, and advise you of the most tax efficient approach every year. We benchmark all of our clients so we can help them identify ways to improve the performance of their business, and how they can make it happen. We will help you earn more, keep more, and enjoy your business more.

Who We Love To Work With

We don't want to work for businesses in regulated sectors, like solicitors or doctors. We want to work with entrepreneurial business owners. Given our geographical area, these people often run businesses in the tourism and leisure, manufacturing, construction, or consultancy sectors.

There is no upper limit on the size of business we will take on. Although we do work with smaller businesses, most of our clients' turnover is between £100,000 and £1,000,000 a year (and appreciate being helped up a quartile).

We're especially happy to work with start-ups who want that helping hand to make sure their business survives and thrives. We offer a special package for start-ups who want to be successful. If their business is just a stop gap until they find a job then we aren't the accountants for them.

To enable us to work closely with our clients during the year, we especially like people who are willing to use Cloud accounting systems. These let us advise you based on how the business is doing now rather than how it did a year ago. This makes our advice far more useful!

We predominately work with businesses based in Devon, Cornwall and Somerset, but if you're happy to connect remotely, then distance is not a problem.

MERLIN
ACCOUNTANCY SERVICES LTD

Merlin Accountancy Services Ltd

AVN Accountant

Exeter, Devon

Email Giles Corby **giles.corby@merlin-accountants.co.uk**

Phone **01392 272972**

Website **www.merlin-accountants.co.uk**

About Our Practice

We work closely with our clients and act for a broad range of business and personal clients.

Apart from the more general accountancy services we can also assist you with business development and specialist tax services.

Our philosophy is always to do our utmost to:
- Provide friendly, courteous and efficient service
- Always exceed your expectations
- Listen to what YOU are saying
- Communicate with you quickly and fully
- Never surprise you with bills you're not expecting
- Be honest, truthful and upfront with you at all times
- Aim for you to pay the least amount of tax payable within the law
- Provide proactive business advice wherever possible

Why We Are Different

Each year we carry out a diagnostic review of our clients' businesses, to identify strategies that could add a very significant amount to their business and/or personal bank account.

In addition we benchmark their businesses across up to 19 key business measures and produce a one page report showing how their business is performing compared with similar businesses. In that report we also carry out some calculations to investigate the possible impact on their profit and cash balances, improving some of those key measures in line with the top performing firms.

Who We Love To Work With

We will act for most business sectors but the firm does not act for charities, solicitors, insurance brokers, doctors or other regulated business sectors.

There is an upper limit on the size of business we will take on of £5million.

We want to work closely with clients… therefore we must like each other!

The client must be based within a half hour's drive of Exeter so that it is easy to meet.

Numbers (UK) Limited

AVN Accountant
Plymouth, Devon
Email **Steven Carey steven@numbersukltd.com**
Phone **01752 226084**
Website **www.numbersukltd.com**

About Our Practice

Numbers (UK) Limited is a truly proactive firm specialising in tax mitigation and succession planning for family companies and business owners. Using leading edge software we take time to discover your personal and business goals, and create a roadmap to take you from where you are now, to where you'd like to be. Our software can show you where improvements can be made, the impact of small changes to your current practices, and the priorities you should set to achieve the quickest gains. All prices are fixed in advance and our pricing software shows each element, so there's no hidden fees. Payments by Direct Debit make it easier to budget too.

Who We Love To Work With

- The ideal client will be a highly profitable, growing business, with multiple outlets/departments/profit centres.

- They will be looking to develop the next generation of manager/owners and will be open to employee participation in the ownership of the business.

- They will be happy to pay premium fees, provided they are convinced that benefits outweigh the cost, and will not abuse our fee guarantee.

- The ideal client will listen to our advice, follow it, be happy to refer others to us, and pay in accordance with our terms (Direct Debit or standing order as an alternative).

- Ideally, we will get on with them on a personal level, and they will buy the full range of services from us.

- The client will provide responses and information in accordance with our procedures

- Our preferred market is the professional services sector, which can include IFAs, solicitors, engineers, architects and any 'scaleable' business.

- Alternatively, they will have a business plan that demonstrates these attributes, or will pay for us to construct one with them.

- We will act for well-planned, properly funded startups.

Why We Are Different

Succession planning, helping clients choose whether to work, focus on the 'big' issues, or to take time off.

Tax planning, to ensure they keep as much of their profits as legally possible.

A review of their business and personal expenditure (Our AYR service), helping them avoid wasting money.

Booth&co

Booth & Co

....

AVN Accountant
Brentwood, Essex
Email **Paul Booth info@boothandco.co.uk**
Phone **01277 224666**
Website **www.boothandco.co.uk**

About Our Practice

....

Chartered Certified Accountants and business advisors based in Brentwood, Essex offering a personal and valuable service.

As well as providing the normal services that clients expect from accountants including accounts preparation, self-assessment tax returns, etc, we can also provide various added value services such as profit improvement, benchmarking and tax planning.

Why We Are Different

....

As a trusted advisor, we can assist in improving the value of a business, provide advice on tax mitigation and help you systemise your business so that it does not rely solely on the business owner to help with your work/life balance.

We can also act as non-executive or Virtual Financial Director.

We try to be friendly and approachable and believe that the client/accountant relationship should be enjoyable rather than tiresome.

Who We Love To Work With

Our ideal client will be focused on improving their business such as increasing their profits, increasing the value of their business and personal wealth. Ideally they would be based locally or in London as there will be a strong focus on regular meetings to provide value. Our fees are based on the value of the service.

Prospero Accounting Ltd

AVN Accountant
Manchester, Greater Manchester
Email **Rennie Evans**
rennie.evans@prosperoaccounting.com
Phone **0161 242 7189**
Website **www.prosperoaccounting.com**

About Our Practice

Prospero Accounting Ltd is a professional services and business consulting firm of Chartered Accountants, regulated by the Institute of Chartered Accountants in England and Wales.

We provide a full range of compliance services including accounts, audit, business tax, company secretarial, corporation tax, management accounts, payroll services, personal tax and value added tax (VAT) from our offices in the centre of Manchester.

However, our primary focus is assisting our clients achieve their goals, increase their profitability, improve their cash flow management and ultimately realise the value of their business they aspire to. We do this by getting to understand our clients' business and director/shareholders and what they want to achieve, the particular drivers and issues that face their specific industry and what is preventing them achieve their objectives.

We offer forward thinking, proactive, common sense advice. Our policy is not to employ trainees so you will only receive advice from fully qualified and experienced Chartered Accountants. With our innovative business model 'Prospero' is a virtual firm of accountants with the ability to work quickly anytime, anywhere.

Why We Are Different

Prospero provide a range of business advisory services that will assist you from first starting out in business to the point when you finally decide it is time to hand the business on to new owners or the next generation of you family. From the outset we will work closely with you to understand your objectives and what you want to achieve. With our full range of services we can provide solutions to meet your needs at every stage of your organisation's development including accessing grants from over 8,000 funding pots with over £200 billion worth of grant funding for business growth.

Who We Love To Work With

- Business sector: The firm does not act for solicitors (accounts rules) or doctors but otherwise will act for any business sector
- Location: North West England
- Size: Total turnover £1m – £10m
- Time in business: If in business for less than 12 months they must subscribe to our start-up service. The reason for this is that we only want to act for businesses which want to be

successful and are prepared to listen to our advice... any business that is not prepared to invest in this service is unlikely to be an ideal customer

- Personality: We want to work closely with clients... therefore we must like them! Therefore we work only with clients we like to deal with and who like to deal with us
- Accounting systems: If the client uses manual books and records they must subscribe to our computerised Cloud based book keeping installation
- Terms of business: The client must agree to the basis of our relationship, and particularly our payment terms by Direct Debit or standing order in advance
- Minimum fees: The client's fee must be at least the minimum fee level set for Prospero, which is £2,500. The only exception is tax return only clients approved by a Director with a minimum fee of £250

 **Taylor Accounting**

Sound advice to minimise your tax

Taylor Accounting Ltd

AVN Accountant
Farnborough, Hampshire
Email Sue Taylor **sue.taylor@tayloraccounting.co.uk**
Phone **01252 522 221**
Website **www.tayloraccounting.co.uk**

About Our Practice

Taylor Accounting Ltd: Inspirational Accountants who have fantastic ideas and technology to enable Entrepreneurial business owners like you to create the complete freedom you deserve. They have transformed businesses like yours to realise their goals and vision using cutting edge technology.

They Provide Their Clients With

- More Wealth
- Freedom
- Opportunities
- Stress free life

What Makes Them Different

- The Olympic team worked on marginal gains, improving every component part to increase overall achievement. This is what they do for businesses not only to improve profitability but also creating a more fulfilled life, rewarding people like you for the risk and effort you put in

- Being pro-active and making a positive difference to your business

- Improving your cash flow and profits

- Saving you tax, identifying issues and resolving them

Taylor Accounting are so confident that they offer a money back guarantee if your results do not improve from taking action based on their advice. Contact us on **01252 522 221** or email **theteam@tayloraccounting.co.uk**

Who We Love To Work With

We welcome companies from most sectors of industry but we just love to work for CEO's or company owners that are dynamic, inspirational and interested in developing their business through their entrepreneurial acumen. We are actively looking for those people who currently turn over £500,000 and/or who are looking to move to the next level. Geography is usually not an issue.

Uniquely for accountants Taylor Accounting Ltd work along-side people like you to pin-point what is actually holding you back and then with proven techniques release the negative beliefs you hold to enable you to shine and you'll wonder why you hadn't been able to do this years ago. They use their skills with numbers, fantastic tools plus their combined 50 years experience of seeing what works and closely guide you-ensuring you stay focussed on improving your business and therefore your life.

Xebra Accounting

AVN Accountant
West Fareham, Hampshire
Email Guy Robinson **guy@xebraaccounting.co.uk**
Phone **02380001313**
Website www.**xebraaccounting.co.uk**

About Our Practice

Xebra Accounting is based in Fareham, between Portsmouth and Southampton, on the south coast.

An award winning, modern accounting practice focused on delivering real value to clients, we believe accountants should work with their clients throughout the year, being their Finance Director, on an 'as needs' basis:

- Helping you keep great accounting records, so that you have up to date financial information at all times
- Teaching you how to do accounting tasks, or doing them for you if you prefer
- Keeping a regular watch over your accounting, spotting problems and contacting you if anything looks unusual
- Meeting with you regularly, so we understand your business, and help you focus on achieving your goals
- Coming up with solutions and implementing them if required

- Planning to minimise tax and calculate tax payments well in advance
- Simple, transparent fees, agreed in advance, paid monthly, with no contract to tie you in
- Guaranteed no penalties for missed filing deadlines, giving you peace of mind
- Free telephone calls and ad hoc advice
- Free Cloud accounting software
- Free monthly performance dashboard visually highlighting revenue, profits and cash performance

Why We Are Different

- We know Cloud accounting systems, being one of the first Xero users in 2008. Guy was Xero's Most Valued Professional Partner from 2013 to 2016
- We specialise in presenting financial information in simple understandable formats, using colour and visuals so that clients understand their numbers
- Year-end accounts will be ready within weeks of your year end, and your tax bills calculated well in advance of any deadline
- We are now working on forecasting and predicting where businesses will be in 12 months' time, so that issues can be dealt with before they arise

Who We Love To Work With

We enjoy working with our clients, and they with us. We believe in building great relationships and encouraging contact, so that we can help with financial decisions.

- Typical client turnover is between £200,000 and £5 million
- Most clients are family and owner managed businesses – sole traders, partnerships, and companies
- Most clients recognise they could improve their business and achieve more. Whilst increasing profitability is often the goal, there are plenty of other reasons too, such as delivering more services for no increase in costs – as for many not for profit and charitable entities – or simply working fewer hours to create more time for the family or other interests
- We work with businesses based within about an hour of Fareham (Hampshire) – Bournemouth in the west, Salisbury, Newbury and Basingstoke in the north, and Guildford and Chichester in the east

The team at Xebra Accounting is keen to work with you to help you achieve the business success you deserve. We have a unique, modern approach to our work, and deliver real value to all of our clients.

We look forward to working with you.

Caplan Associates

AVN Accountant
Borehamwood, Hertfordshire
Email **Philip Caplan pmc@developyour.biz**
Phone **020 3191 9369**
Website **www.developyour.biz**

About Our Practice

Caplan Associates is a firm of Chartered Accountants offering accountancy, taxation and business consultancy services to a wide range of individuals, businesses and charities.

Too often business clients are faced with solutions that suit their accountant rather than them. We take time to understand our client's needs and requirements in order that we can together provide the necessary framework that will enable the business to flourish.

With proper systems in place it enables us to work more closely with our clients in order to develop the business and to provide timely and relevant advice.

Above all there are two areas that seem to cause more problems for clients and any other, those our fees and communications.

We operate for the vast majority of assignments an all-inclusive fixed fee approach and for those cases where it is not applicable clients are kept up-to-date with the costs being incurred. We also know many clients feel that there is a lack of personal service and firms that will listen to their needs and requirements. We pride ourselves in offering a personalised and listening approach with our clients.

Who We Love To Work With

We love all our clients, because we don't take on clients that we don't want to work with!

Our ideal clients tend to be businesses with a turnover of between £500,000 to £6,000,000. The most important factor is that the business owners want to grow their business and are not afraid of change!

Clients who want to communicate with us and build a solid and long lasting business relationship.

The majority of our clients are within 50 miles of the office but we do act for enterprises spread all around the UK.

Why We Are Different

As with all forward thinking firms of accountants, we are particularly good at helping our clients identify the life and business goals and working out a strategy to achieve those goals. We love IT and are always looking to see how we can improve our client services by introducing new software. The software is not only for our benefit for that of the client reducing the time they need to be involved in mundane tasks.

The services we offer are adjusted to match with the client's own needs and requirements. No one size fits all!

Meades & Company Limited

AVN Accountant
Watford, Hertfordshire
Email Paul Meades **paul@meadesandco.co.uk**
Phone **01923 800 444**
Website **www.meadesandco.co.uk**

About Our Practice

We provide solutions to grow your profits – and keep them growing.

We believe it is our responsibility to add value to your business by providing innovative, workable solutions to problems. We achieve this by using our knowledge and experience to work closely alongside you, providing regular reviews of your finances as well as offering timely and proactive advice.

What's more, unlike traditional accountants we think to the future, supplying value added services you wouldn't expect from an accounting firm.

To help you avoid the cash flow strains of an annual invoice and avoid penalties for late submissions to HMRC or Companies House, we have a multi-tiered system of service levels, with fixed prices for all the work we do.

We will agree a simple fixed fee with you, in advance, for every piece of work you ask us to do – so you will always know exactly what everything is going to cost before the job even starts.

Overruns are our problem – even if a job takes us longer that we expected, you will never pay more than the agreed fixed fee.

You will always have your financial information in a timely manner, allowing you to make accurate strategic decisions.

Why We Are Different

As a Xero Gold partner we have all the knowledge and experience needed to make the transition to cloud accounting painless. We can even transfer your existing data so you're never without your historical information.

In addition to proactive accountancy services we can help you keep on top of your responsibilities as an employer. With our HR services not only can you be confident you are meeting all compliance requirements, but with appraisals, surveys and more you will get the most from your team too.

Who We Love To Work With

We work with business owners located within 25 miles of Watford and have an annual turnover between £500k and £10m and typically have at least five employees.

Our office is in Watford and we serve you best by being accessible. Whether you need a sounding board for decision making or an in-depth discussion of your finances, we're never far away. So, if you operate within 25 miles of Watford we're here for you.

Our service has the biggest impact for companies with a turnover between £500k and £10m. We can help you save more through streamlining your accounting administration or earn more with careful financial planning.

You should have all the financial rewards you deserve from running your business. Our tax planning service will help you to ensure you never pay more tax than you have to.

If you want the rewards of working with a proactive accountant who is looking out for you and your business all year round, let's talk.

ROBERT A HARRIS & Co
Chartered Management Accountant

Robert A Harris & Co

AVN Accountant
Stevenage, Hertfordshire
Email **Robert Harris roberth@robertaharris.co.uk**
Phone **01438 811771**
Website **www.robertaharris.co.uk**

About Our Practice

We believe it is the duty of an accountant in practice to have the interests of their clients at the very front of everything we do for them. We are there to help our clients build their businesses, develop their teams, to grow the profits generated by the business along with the inherent value that builds over the years and to maximise both the after-tax income available to them and the value realised on exit.

We achieve this by making available to our clients a wealth of knowledge and advice to help them in defining what they want from life and their business and how best to achieve these goals. It takes in development of a Life & Business plan for the owner, development of a strategy to achieve this including how to build the right team, how to motivate them and assess performance along the way. A big part of this is how to system-atise the business, building in resilience and risk management.

We look at helping clients achieve their goals within the financing available, with business forecasting, cash management and using the numbers to inform and educate the team on how the company is doing and their role in its progress. In short we aim to make the journey as profitable.

Who We Love To Work With

Given the huge variability in human nature, culture and behaviour, it is not easy to define our ideal client but there are some characteristics we believe will facilitate a valuable relationship for both sides. Firstly the business can be quite young but probably no younger than 2 years. Secondly the owner must be committed to making it work and not be constantly looking for diversifications or alternatives. The business can be in difficulty, providing the underlying product or service has a good market. Often such businesses can be great opportunities for the owner who finds a great accountant to help them. Thirdly the owner must have a vision of a business greater than himself or herself. The route to wealth is to leverage the skills of others and to find people who are better than the owner at whatever specialism they have. Lastly, the owner must believe there is a way to make this team work cohesively in his or her interests and that they want to develop such a way or process.

We are located in North Hertfordshire and serve clients North of the Thames and in the Northern Home Counties of Bedfordshire, Hertfordshire, Essex and Middlesex.

We offer our clients a business relationship based on a mutual vision of a growing and profitable business. This vision is about a journey we believe they will find both financially rewarding and personally very enjoyable.

We are there for our clients to see them through the tough times and to help them make the most of the opportunities that will come their way.

Calcutt Matthews

AVN Accountant
Ashford, Kent
Email **Nick Hume** **nick.hume@calcutt-m.co.uk**
Phone **01233 623300**
Website **www.calcutt-m.co.uk**

About Our Practice

Multi award winning Kent based firm that excels in growing business and tax reduction.

Why We Are Different

Our latest survey shows that on average a client with 5 – 10 employees will increase average profits after eight quarterly meetings by £193,000. Clients with 10 – 50 employees will on average increase profits by £383,000 in these eight quarters.

On average we saved our client with a turnover of £500,000 £39,000 in taxes.

We also specialise in looking after overseas businesses which want a UK company

Who We Love To Work With

Ideal clients have a turnover of £500k to £30 million and pay our minimum £3000 fee per annum.

We best serve clients in Kent, London and the South East.

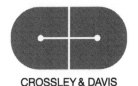

CROSSLEY & DAVIS

Crossley & Davis Limited

AVN Accountant
Herne Bay, Kent
Email Mark Lowton **mark.lowton@crossleydavis.com**
Phone **01227 712714**
Website **www.crossleydavis.com**

About Our Practice

We specialise in providing advanced tax advice and business growth services to help improve your business and personal wealth. We go beyond normal accountancy services, by aiming to be your personal, trusted adviser. As one of our clients said, *"You are my financial doctor."*

We Help Our Clients By Providing

Added Value Accounting Services
In addition to annual accounts and tax, we act as your virtual finance director, proactively making suggestions to improve your profits, cashflow and tax.

Specialist Tax Services
We specialise in business and personal tax, so you can pay less tax. We also go further by being part of a network of tax

consultants who can provide advanced tax planning advice.

Business Growth Services

We provide in-depth information on your business, which has been called 'Sat Nav' for your business. It contains all the key information you need to grow your business, improve your profits, improve your cashflow and increase your personal wealth. Combined with our practical action plans, we can help you to improve your personal wealth.

Who We Love To Work With

We like to work with ambitious, enthusiastic, owner managed businesses who:

Typically have a turnover of £250,000 or more

At this stage the business needs to put the financial systems and business processes in place, to support future growth. This is where we can work with the business owner to not only report on the numbers, but to help improve the numbers as well.

Usually have several employees

With a team in place, we can help with the systems and processes needed to support the team for growth.

Want to grow their businesses, improve their profits and cashflow

Typically, this means the business recognises the need for specific targets and plans to reach those targets.

Are open minded to new ideas
To achieve better results, new approaches are needed and being receptive to new ideas is key.

Are looking for more than annual accounts and tax returns from their accountant
Of course, we deliver these, but we can also deliver a lot more as well.

Embrace new technology including cloud accounting solutions such as Xero
We are certified Xero partners and use technology to make life much easier.

Why We Are Different

We help our clients save money and improve their financial wealth, through:

Advanced tax planning
We help our clients save significant amounts of tax. For example, we recently helped a client reclaim over £40,000 in tax. We also identified £80,000 of tax savings for a client by restructuring their business.

Business Growth services
We help our clients improve their business profits and grow. For example, we recently helped a client turn his business from breakeven into an annual profit of £50,000 and his business continues to grow profitably.

haleys
business advisers

Haleys Business Advisers Limited

AVN Accountant
Preston, Lancashire
Email Andrew Davis **andrew.davis@haleysba.co.uk**
Phone **01772 741200**
Website **www.haleysba.co.uk**

About Our Practice

The why?

If you're the sort of person who wants to enjoy running a great business, and care about people – then we can show you how.

The how?

Through a carefully developed programme, we show you how to take more control over your life and in the process:

- Increase profitability
- Maximise capital value
- Protect your assets
- And make it more enjoyable

The what?

We just happen to be accountants who take an interest in helping business owners succeed.

Haleys business advisors provide financial, taxation and commercial expertise to established business owners in order to help them increase profitability, maximise capital value, protect their assets and enjoy life to the full.

Why We Are Different

In order for us to help established business owners increase profitability, maximise capital value, protect their assets and enjoy life to the full – we need to establish an intimate working relationship.

We understand it is essential that we understand the industry in which our clients operate. We talk 'their language' and empathise with the wider issues facing them. We then challenge our clients to articulate both their personal and business goals and help them achieve those objectives in a logical and structured manner.

As a result, we become key trusted advisors not just accountants.

Who We Love To Work With

If you are an established business owner with a desire to grow your business and create value, but find yourself too busy working in the business on a daily basis and aren't able to spend enough quality time driving your business forward, we can help you.

As a firm we work closely with our clients to ensure we understand their business and their requirements and together we can develop a trusted working relationship.

We focus on making small changes across all areas of your business which in turn can make a big impact on your profitability and capital value.

Business size or location does not matter to us, but our clients must share our philosophies and ideas and be willing to work with us to identify these areas of improvement and focus.

Our results speak for themselves with many of our clients experiencing over 50% growth in pre-tax profit since working with us.

If you want to work smarter, increase your profitability and capital value, you are our ideal client.

HIGHWOODS & ASSOCIATES
CERTIFIED PUBLIC ACCOUNTANTS

Highwoods & Associates

AVN Accountant

London

Email Mo Barrie **mobarrie@highwoodsandassociates.co.uk**

Phone **0207 979 2000**

Website **www.highwoodsandassociates.co.uk**

About Our Practice

If you are looking for top quality accountants, then look no further! Highwoods & Associates is a highly rated accounting practice, providing personalised, quality service and its environs with services ranging from tax preparation to general account-ancy for small business owners and individuals alike.

Our goal is to provide our clients with the highest quality serv-ices, provided in a friendly, courteous, and efficient manner. Our philosophy centres around doing our best, aiming to exceed your expectations on all fronts, with every job.

With the understanding that communication is the most important part of providing quality service, our accountants ensure they take the time to listen to you, answer your questions, and communicate quickly and fully. As a customer oriented firm, we aim to provide you with the best, honest, friendly and efficient service in the area. Such a promise from us means that we get it done, not only as promised and on time, but we exceed expectations on all fronts. If you still have questions, feel free to call us today for your free consultation, and we will assist you in every way that we can.

Who We Love To Work With

At Highwoods & Associates, we are looking for clients we can maintain a high level of personal relationship with thereby ensuring a wider range of interaction which raises trust and long-term commitments.

Our clients do not feel on their own because we do not only help with financial accounting but also on developing their business and making tax efficiency decisions for the organisation.

Why We Are Different

Our goals are to:
- Provide an efficient and reliable accounting support to the business.
- Sound financial advice based on regularly evaluating the client's financial records.
- Strategic advice on the long term and the sustainable success of the business.

The key element of our business philosophy is regular communication with the client. We always ensure that the client is updated at all the stages of our accounting procedures with regular reports for the client's reference.

Solid Limited

AVN Accountant
Clerkenwell, London
Email Arber Pacarada **arber@solid.accountants**
Phone **03333 443 993**
Website **www.solid.accountants**

About Our Practice

We are a hard working team dedicated to protecting and galvanising your business. Your targets are our targets. Your goals are our goals. We are business owners ourselves and we do understand business. Together we will build solid foundations for your business, enabling you grow to the successes you need to grow and thrive. Solid is built upon a solid mission statement. Everything that we do, say, type, advise, submit and calculate will be done with excellence, with integrity and with transparency.

Why We Are Different

We believe that it takes more than a single meeting to measure up an accountant. You will trust us. You will rely on our advice. You will speak to us often. You can't gauge all of that in a single meeting. So we don't ask anybody to pay us a penny in the first three months. During this time we will put in place bookkeeping and accounting processes that not only will save the business time and money, but also improve operations in other areas of the business. If you like our style, we will carry on collaborating. If you are unhappy, we will part company with no hard feelings.

Who We Love To Work With

We work with established businesses and startups with ambitious plans for growth. We work closely with our clients, so they have to be within Greater London area. We work well particularly with restaurateurs and successful cafe owners as well as with architects, design studios and artists.

btp Associates

AVN Accountant
Merthyr Tydfil
Email **Huw Baker hb@btpassoc.co.uk**
Phone **01685 384375**
Website **www.btpassoc.co.uk**

About Our Practice

We are a firm of Chartered Accountants offering accountancy and business consultancy services to owner managed and family owned businesses across South Wales.

We are the largest firm of Chartered Accountants based in the heads of the valleys of South Wales. We currently have six qualified team members boasting over a hundred years of hands on experience of working with, and advising business owners.

Our mission is to help our clients and our team to achieve their goals. Our core purpose is to provide our clients with a full range of services that allows them to grow their businesses, increase their net worth, have more free time and the peace of mind necessary to pursue other activities, enjoy their families and generally help them to achieve their goals.

Why We Are Different

We work far more closely with our clients than traditional accountants. We also have a smaller number of clients than normal, and are selective as to the clients we act for. We want to get to know our clients' businesses inside out, enabling us to easily identify problems and spot opportunities. We want to help improve profits and encourage growth.

LAWRENCE & CO
Chartered Accountants

Lawrence & Co

AVN Accountant
Harrow, Middlesex
Email **Jay Chatwani Jay@lawacc.co.uk**
Phone **0208 4249777**
Website **www.lawacc.co.uk**

About Our Practice

We must be doing something right if we can win the AVN Accounting Firm of the Year – Rising Star award for 2013/14! That something is the total dedication towards our clients and our people. We are approachable, available and affordable. That means: We answer all incoming calls within two rings and we never interrogate you with silly questions like *"who is calling?"* or *"what is it about?"* but put you through to the person you wish to speak with straightaway.

You may speak with any person of your choice – including the partners. We have no barriers.

Your queries to us can be on subjects outside our terms of engagement with you. We will help wherever we can.

If more convenient to you, we can arrange meetings outside normal office hours, even on Saturdays and Sundays.

On receipt of all information by the relevant date, we promise to complete the assignment (your accounts, tax returns etc.) within 20 working days.

Our fees are fixed in advance. You will never receive a surprise bill from us. Never. Our fees include:

- Unlimited free phone support
- Unlimited free meetings
- and lots of other benefits

Why We Are Different

Our philosophy is always to do our utmost to…

- Provide friendly, courteous and efficient service
- Always exceed your expectations
- Listen to what YOU are saying
- Communicate with you quickly and fully
- Never surprise you with bills you're not expecting
- Be honest, truthful and upfront with you at all times
- Aim for you to pay the least amount of tax payable within the law
- Provide proactive business advice wherever possible

Who We Love To Work With

We like to work with people who are similar to us – ambitious! Clients who want their businesses to go places and who are open minded to seek and listen to advice. It does not matter where you are located – we have clients all over the world. What matters is your burning desire to create a great success of your business. We will show you the rest!

RCG & Co

AVN Accountant
North Harrow, Middlesex
Email **Raj Gosrani raj@rcg.co.uk**
Phone **020 8424 9755**
Website **www.rcg.co.uk**

About Our Practice

We are different to other accountants. We work much more closely with our clients than traditional accountants. We also have a far smaller number of clients than normal and are selective in the clients we act for. We want to get to know our clients' businesses inside out, enabling us to easily identify problems and spot opportunities. We want to help improve profits and encourage growth.

Our mission is to always add value. Whatever we do for you, we will always carry out our work with the aim of adding value to your business. We run a very cost effective business by making the most of modern technology, but we will never be the cheapest solution. That is why our overall aim is to assist you to:

- Grow your business
- Increase your wealth
- Spend time doing the things that you really want to do

Why We Are Different

We do the whole range of compliance work from accounts to tax. In addition we do cash flow forecasting including measuring your KPIs, inheritance tax planning, tax minimisation service and acting as your Virtual Finance Director. We use Cloud bookkeeping solutions which enhance record keeping and measurability of profits and cash flow. We do group structures and tax efficient planning. We have links with USA, Singapore and India.

Who We Love To Work With

Our ideal clients are owner managed businesses in a wide range of business sectors with turnover up to £25 million. We also look after inward investment into UK, for example subsidiaries of offshore companies. We do statutory audit work. We are interested in clients who wish to grow their businesses. We are based in London and service businesses in London and the South East.

Kirby & Haslam

AVN Accountant
King's Lynn, Norfolk
Email Neil Kirby **neil.kirby@kirbyandhaslam.com**
Phone **01553 761316**
Website **www.kirbyandhaslam.com**

About Our Practice

Kirby and Haslam are one of Norfolk's leading accountancy firms. We are an established practice with over 30 years' experience in the industry. We are based in King's Lynn, but we have clients from a much wider area including Norfolk, Cambridgeshire and Lincolnshire, as well as a number of clients from much further afield.

We provide our services to many types of businesses including start-ups, sole traders and small companies through to medium and large enterprises, from all manner of trade sectors, including manufacture, construction, retail & tourism to name just a few.

Our experience in the industry means that we are adept in helping your business grow to face the challenges encountered by businesses today. Furthermore, we are able to help you develop your business into the successful operation you've always aimed for. We pride ourselves on the fast, efficient and friendly service provided by our experienced team.

At Kirby and Haslam, we are totally committed to providing our clients with a service tailored to their individual needs. We keep track of all the essentials for you and with over 30 years in the industry, we are able to provide advice on how to add value to your performance.

Why We Are Different

Clients prefer us because our passion shines through everything we do. We are dedicated to finding new ways to generate value for our clients. It is our desire to go the extra mile to help you achieve success for you to be happy. The consultation meeting will ensure we understand what you require in the short and long term. It will then be mutually decided how we can help you achieve these goals, and all at a fixed fee decided up front, thus allowing you opportunity to assess the cost to achieve your ambitions, whether that is saving tax or building a successful business or anything else.

Who We Love To Work With

We are looking to act for people in a variety of industries including:

- Construction
- Manufacturing
- Retail
- Travel & Tourism

- Engineering
- Professional Services

It is preferable that your location is within 50 miles of Kings Lynn, but this is not completely necessary as we already act for businesses in Kent, Lancashire and Cumbria.

Whether you are in a start up situation or are an established business we will assess whether we can help you achieve your business and personal ambitions. At the initial meet, whether online or in person it can be assessed that both sides consider we are mutually compatible and can forge a future together. If we are going to work closely with you to help you build your business there has to be common ground to build that relationship. You will need to be ambitious and wish to build a successful business so that we can help you fulfil this goal. We believe in maintaining close and regular contact with our clients to guide them through the accounts and financial aspects of their business in a straightforward manner.

Phipps Henson McAllister

AVN Accountant
Kingsthorpe, Northamptonshire
Email Ross Phipps **r.phipps@phm-accountants.co.uk**
Phone **01604 718866**
Website **www.phm-accountants.co.uk**

About Our Practice

We are a firm of Chartered Accountants based in Northampton and Banbury, offering accounts, taxation, business advisory and support services to a wide range of businesses and individuals across Northamptonshire, Oxfordshire and surrounding areas.

At Phipps Henson McAllister we provide a cost-effective, solution to meet all of your financial needs. We work closely with our clients in order to deliver timely, individual advice on how to improve your business and personal wealth.

Why We Are Different

Helping You Achieve Your Goals
We don't just prepare accounts, we can help business owners achieve both their business and personal goals.

Full Range Of Accountancy & Business Advisory Services

We offer a complete solution that includes many additional services, including goal setting and planning, systemising the business, book keeping, management accounting, payroll and company secretarial services.

Probate

We are also now one of the first firms of Chartered Accountants to be licensed to carry out the reserved legal activity of non-contentious probate by the ICAEW.

Who We Love To Work With

We have three ideal client profiles:

Start-Ups

A start-up business looking for advice on how to be guided through the first few years. We help our clients with everything they need to start in business from identifying the appropriate business structure and registering the business/forming a company through to business advice, cash flow forecasting and then recommending the appropriate book keeping solution.

Established Businesses

An established business who may be looking for that little bit extra advice or guidance. Our solutions can allow you to free up time, explore further tax savings, obtain regular support/advice or simply ensure you comply with all current regulations.

Contractor/Freelancer

A contractor/freelancer who simply needs to ensure they comply and keep their tax to a minimum. We provide simple and tax efficient offerings to ensure we look after your filing requirements with Companies House and HMRC.

Bambury & Co

AVN Accountant
Bicester, Oxfordshire
Email **Patrick Cracroft-Brennan patrickcb@bambury.info**
Phone **01869 222830**
Website **www.bambury.info**

About Our Practice

We are a small firm of Chartered Accountants based in Bicester in North Oxfordshire. Should this be a problem? Certainly not. We might be small, but we have a big presence on the Internet and handle clients from all around the country. Unlike the larger accountancy practices, we provide a more personal and flexible service to our clients.

We are passionate about business start-ups who have the ambition and drive to grow – these companies are the future! We use proven methodologies, particularly out new business support programme 'Start Up,' to help growth-minded new businesses survive their crucial first twelve months. We can help you prepare business plans, cash flow forecasts and profit forecasts. We will show you how to keep a close watch on your new business using Cloud based software so that we both know it is performing to expectations.

Why We Are Different

Bambury & Co was one of the first firms of Chartered Accountants authorised to carry out non-contentious probate work. We offer a professional will writing and probate service and specialise in carrying out succession planning reviews for business owners.

Who We Love To Work With

We are always looking for clients who share our ethos. Our ideal client profile would be an owner managed business with huge ambitions to grow. We want to add value to your business and make those plans a reality.

When we review your annual accounts with you we don't just look back to the past. We look forward to the future by carrying out a free diagnostic review to see which improvements will increase your profits. Part of the diagnostic review is a benchmarking exercise to see how you perform against others in your industry, profession or trade. We will use sophisticated remuneration planning software to show you the right mix between salaries and dividends.

Murray Associates

....

AVN Accountant

Paisley, Renfrewshire

Email Gloria Murray **gloria@murrayassoc.co.uk**

Phone **0141 889 4247**

Website **www.murrayassociates.co.uk**

About Our Practice

....

Gloria started her own accountancy practice in 1996 in order to help small and micro businesses to understand their finances and help them grow their business. After years working in a variety of business fields, Gloria decided to study to become an accountant. She realised there was a gap in the market for accountants with real life business knowledge and wanted to develop her financial skills to help small business. The mission of Murray Associates is to create profitable small businesses that sustain local communities, provide progressive work opportunities and care for the planet.

She has continued this work and in her support role to micro and small business owners Gloria has developed a series of mentoring programmes which resulted in her becoming the Most Innovative Accountant in the UK and named as one of the World's Most Inspiring Accountants.

The knowledge of the numbers, good tax planning and a holistic approach as business advisor, coach and mentor has been described as invaluable. By holding you accountable for taking action on the key areas of your business, you can achieve the results you want and deserve.

Why We Are Different

Our profit improvement programmes take you from being self-employed to business owner to entrepreneur.

We have a strong understanding of results marketing for small business owners and use learned and earned real life business skills and experience to get a true feel of your business that allows us to resolve your problems, issues and challenges and provide unique solutions in a practical manner.

A proven track record of increasing clients' profits while maintaining their life work balance means you, like them, achieve more both in business and in your life.

Who We Love To Work With

Businesswomen in the service sector are ideally suited to what we do. They may work in hair & beauty; lifestyle & health or be professional therapists; coaches, trainers or consultants. You can access your accounts information on the Cloud so you have your numbers at your fingertips. You only need access to the Internet through a mobile phone, iPad or laptop.

Our ideal client is 'a very bright woman but doesn't really recognise this. She's in a long-term relationship with children she adores. She worries that she's missing out on seeing them grow up as she works long hours and rarely has time for holidays. She feels if she split up with her partner she would struggle to get by as she has no real savings. She likes being around people and is passionate about what she does. She's open to new ideas and knows she needs to get stuff right in order to build her future. She is driven and wants to be perfect. This sometimes stops her from getting on with stuff in business. She feels she doesn't understand the numbers, but doesn't want to ask her accountant to explain things as it makes her feel inadequate and vulnerable.'

I understand... Gloria Murray, Queen of Profit and the Woman's Accountant.

Tranter Lowe

AVN Accountant
Telford, Shropshire
Email Jon Poole **jon@tranterlowe.com**
Phone **01952 619161**
Website **www.tranterlowe.com**

About Our Practice

Tranter Lowe is a progressive and forward thinking firm combining 75 years of experience with the knowledge of a trusted advisor to provide a first class professional service to local business owners and individuals.

We understand that the quality of the compliance work we undertake on behalf of clients is vitally important but not particularly rewarding. Through precise planning, starting with a fixed fee quote and work programme, clients know they can depend on this service with absolute certainty for the management of their business.

Our level of involvement is tailored to suit – it can begin with book-keeping, if required, and payroll/auto-enrolment support.

We do offer much more than this. Our focus is to provide clients with useful and relevant advice, including profit extraction and efficient remuneration, tax planning, cash flow forecasting and management accounting, performance measurement and improvement.

From business start-ups requiring support and mentoring, to established enterprises in need of retirement and exit strategies, we are very proud of the trust placed in us and our involvement in helping our clients' businesses becoming more successful and enjoyable to run.

Why We Are Different

We think the following sets us apart from other local accountants:
- Fixed fees, agreed before work begins, to ensure no unpleasant surprises
- Reasonable access to our team at no extra cost
- All our work is programmed and agreed with clients in advance
- An annual checklist to help ensure that you don't pay any more tax than you need to, considering the most tax efficient remuneration and business structure
- An annual review of the services we provide, to make sure that you're getting exactly what you want from us
- We use plain English, so that you know what we're talking about

Who We Love To Work With

Our ideal clients are local established small and medium sized enterprises who are looking forward to growing and improving their numbers – both business and personal – often needing assistance with the measurement of business performance.

However, we are very pleased to be approached by start-ups who want to work closely with us to create a successful business that is both enjoyable and rewarding to run.

At the other end of the spectrum, we always encourage clients to consider their exit strategy – often planning many years ahead – to get their businesses in shape to maximise the value of their retirement.

At the same time, we offer an efficient personal tax return service for individuals and micro enterprises.

We also provide a payroll bureau service including the implementation and administration of the current auto-enrolment pension regulations.

In all cases, our initial interview is a 'no-obligation/free of charge' meeting to determine a client's exact needs, agree our approach and to ensure we can work together.

Lewis Ballard

....

AVN Accountant
Cardiff, South Glamorgan
Email Neil Ballard **neilB@lewisballard.co.uk**
Phone **02920 735502**
Website www.lewisballard.co.uk

About Our Practice

....

As a fast growing firm of 23 based in Cardiff, we provide consultancy and advisory services to SME's throughout the UK. Our holistic approach, includes business development, business coaching, tax planning, IHT services, trusts and wealth management. We help you, from business start up to exit strategy, to maximise profits and protect and retain as much income as possible. We also provide routine accounts, tax, VAT and payroll.

We are both Xero and Crunchboard Gold members, to give innovative Cloud accounting, business analysis solutions and up to the minute advice.

Our main focus is adding value to your business and balance to your life, by asking what you want and helping you achieve it. Balance isn't a one size fits all. If business is great, but there's no family time, we help build a business to give you more. If, however, you are happy with your life balance and just want to build your bank balance, we help maximise your profits. And if it's a bit of both we help with that too! We aim to keep your personal and business finances in balance. So you don't put everything into keeping business afloat, without having two pins personally, or end up with nothing to even retire on.

Why We Are Different

Our approach differs from many other accountants. For a start, we don't just give you the numbers; we explain what they mean and how to improve them. Our focus is adding value to your business and balance to your life.

We are both Xero and Crunchboard Gold members, to give the most innovative Cloud accounting, business analysis solutions and up to the minute advice. We also trained with top marketing/business experts, Michael Heppell, Peter Thompson and Tony Robbins on latest marketing strategies and are IMA practitioners to help you improve how you connect with your team and customers.

Who We Love To Work With

We have 30 years of specialist knowledge in the Dental and Healthcare sector, and these clients make up about 40% of our businesses. As healthcare specialists we also have strong links with healthcare specialist bank managers, solicitors, IFAs and many other professionals, so we have the contacts to help you succeed, whatever your needs.

We also work with a full range of professions, from surveyors to electricians and restaurants to hairdressers, high net worth individuals and several celebrities. We find that whatever the sector, business owners often face the same issues and that's where we can help.

Our ideal client is fundamentally a business we can help, one which is looking to grow and change. Our main aim is to make a difference. We want to work with people who are looking for specialist advice which they are willing to follow. And, most importantly, we only work with nice people, who we can respect and respect us too.

Chartered Accountants

Butt Miller Limited

AVN Accountant
Camberley, Surrey
Email Roland Moss **roland.moss@buttmiller.co.uk**
Phone **01276 25542**
Website **www.buttmiller.co.uk**

About Our Practice

Butt Miller are a team of Chartered Accountants in Surrey, providing clients both in the Home Counties and nationwide with a comprehensive service and an attitude to accountancy that sets us apart from the rest.

Our aim is to help you see your bigger financial picture. This means we want to do more than just help out with compliance.

Adding value is our company's core motivation, so instead of just helping you with the small things we put everything in perspective. With the little details sorted out the picture of your financial future becomes clearer.

A service bundle built around your own accounting requirements is the frame to your bigger financial picture. We have bundles for individuals looking for advice on things like

Inheritance Tax all the way to large businesses looking to fully outsource their finances.

We can help relieve the stress of running a small business on a tight budget, to providing a comprehensive accounting package for established and ambitious businesses looking to grow into the future.

Why We Are Different

We take a holistic overview to your business to help you achieve your financial goals. We work with business owners to develop their businesses to work for them and not the other way round. We do this in a number of ways, by offering strategic planning days, allowing our clients to outsource the running of their finance departments to us (or just the bookkeeping), allowing for improved cash flow and informed decision making, attending quarterly board meetings as the FD, preparation of management accounts and profit/cash flow forecasts so you understand where your business is financially

Who We Love To Work With

Our ideal client is either a business owner or individual who is looking to receive business and financial advice and support in helping them to grow and develop their business, along with tax advice to help them capitalise on appropriate tax planning opportunities. We have developed our expertise in a number of niche sectors which include creative, digital, marketing agencies, property construction with the related trade services, IT, scientific and geotechnical services.

Goddards Accountants Kingston

AVN Accountant
West Molesey, Surrey
Email **Derek Williamson derek@gandco.co.uk**
Phone **0208 941 2187**
Website **www.cloudaccountingsurrey.co.uk**

About Our Practice

Using Cloud based accountancy software, Goddards work with clients in 'real time' on the 'today and tomorrow,' rather than telling a client what we have done after we have done it.
We are fully accredited for Personal and Corporate Taxation work.
We are fully accredited for Probate work.

Why We Are Different

- We write wills
- We benchmark our clients' businesses
- We put them efficiently into 'The Cloud'

Who We Love To Work With

Our ideal client is sold on the idea of 'Cloud based accounting,' using add ons such as Receipts Bank and Satago, to improve the processing and back office functions of the business.

Ideally they should also be using a Cloud based 'Contact Management' system to improve sales conversions.

Goddards are looking for firms which can then use the 'Cloud based software' to enable them to also act as their part time Finance Director.

Goddards will also want to be allowed to 'benchmark' the client, and to provide 'personal balance sheets' for each Director of the company.

Grant-Jones Accountancy Ltd

AVN Accountant
Camberley, Surrey
Email Fiona Jones **fiona@grant-jonesaccountancy.com**
Phone **01276 682 588**
Website **www.grant-jonesaccountancy.com**

About Our Practice

Established in 2006 Grant-Jones Accountancy Ltd was founded by Fiona Jones, who is passionate about helping clients to achieve their dreams and great things for their business.

As Chartered Management Accountants we don't just deal with the compliance of your business, we specialise in business planning and cash flow forecasting, working with you to focus on your future and to achieve your goals. We are also Chartered Tax Advisers, so we make sure you pay the right amount of tax and not a penny more.

Grant-Jones staff are qualified by exams and business experience. With many years of training in Industry, we talk your language, we understand the problems you face, as we also run a successful, fast growing business too. We have faced the same problems you have, and using the right key performance metrics we can drive business performance in the right direction.

We offer a range of packaged services, from our Incubator package suitable for fast growing start up businesses to our Total Accounting Solution for more established businesses.

Give us your past and we'll show you the future.

Who We Love To Work With

We love to work with small to medium sized businesses, who want to change their lives for the better. They are based in the Surrey, Berkshire and Hampshire region. They are led by motivated individuals who are passionate about their business and want to make a difference to their community. We believe that working for your passion should be something enjoyable not a chore.

Small to medium sized businesses often have problems with cash flow because they are growing fast. When you are growing, cash is the life blood of the business, but there is never enough to go around, resulting in the inevitable growing pains. We meet with our clients on a regular basis to help them plan their growth and make sure there is enough cash available at the critical time. We work in partnership with the business owner, after all, his or her success is our success – his or her failure is our failure.

Sometimes growing businesses have problems finding the right staff when they need them the most. We help our clients to analyse their business processes, to understand where the weaknesses and gaps are.

Why We Are Different

We have a background in industry, trained in companies just like yours.

A new client recently explained why he had moved to Grant-Jones Accountancy Ltd. He said *"...it's like the business owners speak English but the Accountants speak Portuguese. To make matters worse the Bank manager is speaking in Spanish!"* We all need to get on the same page and speak the same language.

When we take on a new client we conduct a free business review of your processes and systems. We take the time to get to know you and your business, and we can identify any gaps or in-efficiencies in your processes.

IDH ACCOUNTANCY.

IDH Accountancy Services Limited

AVN Accountant
Worcester Park, Surrey
Email Ifan Lloyd **info@idhaccountancy.com**
Phone **020 3411 4401**
Website **www.idhaccountancy.com**

About Our Practice

IDH Accountancy combines the personal touch of a small firm with the experience and expertise of a big business to provide every client with a bespoke service that meets their needs. As qualified accountants, we are able to provide a comprehensive range of services to our clients from personal tax, corporation tax and VAT returns to company accounts, company secretarial work and payroll services.

However, preparing accounts is just the start of what we can do. We specialise in using this information to help you get the most from your business and your personal finances, and enjoy an easier life. When we meet, we will talk you through the services we offer, all the options we recommend for you, and let you know what the price will be. It's then up to you how much or how little you would like us to do for you. We will also let you know what you could do yourself to reduce the fee – after all, it's important to us that you are happy with the value of the work we're doing for you.

Why We Are Different

Ifan has over 30 years' commercial experience in a range of businesses from SMEs to multinationals. With a history of making a sustained contribution to a company's profitability, IDH Accountancy combines accountancy expertise with customer management, sales and marketing knowledge to help our clients maximise the potential of their business.

Most importantly, we want to make a real difference to our clients. And as a small business ourselves, we are ideally placed to understand and advise on all the challenges faced by our clients, and work with them to make their business a success.

Who We Love To Work With

We are based in Worcester Park, Surrey, so most of our clients operate in South West London or Surrey, although as we use Cloud accounting software with our clients, we can easily provide a hands-on service wherever they are working from.

We work with sole traders, partnerships and limited companies, and specialise in helping businesses grow by engaging them with the financial opportunities available. Many of our clients are from the creative sector, and as approved experts with the Design Business Association, we have many years' experience of managing the specific needs of designers. However, we are equally placed to add value to clients in the construction, retail and service industries, to name just a few.

We recommend that all our clients use Cloud accounting software for their bookkeeping. The latest accounting software makes managing your finances quicker, easier – and cheaper – for you. We can help set you up with the most appropriate options for your business, and advise on additional products that may help you.

Bell Anderson

....

AVN Accountant
Gateshead, Tyne and Wear
Email Geoff Little **geofflittle@bellanderson.co.uk**
Phone **0191 4901444**
Website **www.bellanderson.co.uk**

About Our Practice

....

A local firm of business people who are Chartered Accountants with in excess of 150 years of experience at senior management level. The firm was 'established' as Bell Anderson in March 1993 when Stan Bell and Michael Anderson launched the firm. Geoff Little joined the business some years later to further develop the rapidly expanding business as it moved from Newcastle City Centre to Gateshead. We are a small highly qualified team. All of the senior management have trained with and worked for the top four International firms of Chartered Accountants as well as having significant industrial experience. We work very closely with a select targeted client base building on strong personal relationships. After all as our strap line goes 'It's a people thing.'

Why We Are Different

....

Clients comment that what they value most from us is:

- We make a vital contribution to their success
- We help clients see the wood from the trees
- We challenge their business assumptions
- We ask the difficult questions people would sometimes prefer to brush under the carpet

We encourage 'slow thinking' but 'fast action' – that means the ability to draw rational conclusions from a full analysis of the facts, summarising the results, calculating the options and then acting quickly and decisively. This kind of input is priceless.

Who We Love To Work With

Well, we do it with our ideal clients and who are they? If we feel that we can't make a significant contribution to helping you achieve your goals, then we are not right for each other. Therefore we have established three criteria which someone has to meet before we agree to take them on as a client:

1. We must like you – life is too short to waste time working with people you don't like
2. We must be able to help you achieve your goals – this is one of our core values
3. We must be able to create a story out of our relationship – helping clients to succeed and then asking you, the client, to either write a testimonial as to how we have helped you, recount your experiences at a presentation and/or record a video for future marketing use

James, Stanley & Co. Limited

....

AVN Accountant
Birmingham, West Midlands
Email Jayne Cox **andrew@jamesstanley.co.uk**
Phone **0121 706 8585**
Website **www.jamesstanley.co.uk**

About Our Practice

....

James, Stanley & Co. was established in 1922 and has remained a family firm ever since. The current Managing Director of the company is Andrew James who trained with Touche, Ross & Co. before joining the family firm some years after qualification.

The firm is located on the A45 in South Yardley, Birmingham but we service clients all over the country – from Oban to Hastings.

We currently have a highly skilled team of ten which includes two Chartered Accountants, two Certified Accountants and an Accounting Technician. All of our team offer a personable and dedicated approach to the clients which they service.

Historically the firm offered compliance services in the areas of audit, accounts preparation, personal and corporate tax, payroll and VAT. In 2009 the firm joined AVN and has since delivered a complete range of business growth and tax planning services. As a result, the company has grown year on year and at the same time we have made a profound difference to our clients' businesses.

We embrace the latest technology available to the accounting profession and we promote Cloud based solutions to our clients in order to provide them with the best possible service.

Why We Are Different

James, Stanley & Co. Limited has been recognised for the outstanding proactive service it delivers to its clients. The company features in two independently written books which highlight excellence of service within the accountancy profession.

The books entitled 'The UK's Best Accounting Practices' and 'The World's Most Inspiring Accountants' were compiled after extensive research was carried out by the authors and the firm is extremely proud to be featured in both.

As a result James, Stanley & Co. Ltd can genuinely claim excellence in service delivery to its clients.

Who We Love To Work With

We currently act for a wide range of sectors, including manufacturing, the service sector, retail and education to clients who are based all over the country.

Our business growth and tax planning services are best suited to businesses which have the following characteristics:

- Sales of between £200,000 and £10 million per annum
- Businesses who are seriously looking to improve their profitability
- Businesses who are happy to take on board our recommendations
- Business owners who are prepared to take action with the plans we put forward
- Most of our clients are owner managed businesses
- It is vital that we have a rapport with our clients' management teams and enjoy working together
- Our clients must be prepared to meet with us on a regular basis in order for us to truly make a difference to their business

We are happy to meet with start-ups and smaller businesses so long as they have ambitions to grow and are looking for our help on that journey.

thomasnockmartin⁺

CHARTERED ACCOUNTANTS

Thomas Nock Martin Limited

AVN Accountant
Brierley Hill, West Midlands
Email Simon Nock **simon-nock@tnmca.com**
Phone **01384 261300**
Website **www.tnmca.com**

About Our Practice

Thomas Nock Martin is a progressive black country firm of Chartered Accountants based at the Waterfront, Brierley Hill in the West Midlands.

We do all the things you would expect from great accountants. We will prepare your annual accounts and tax returns and generally steer you through the red tape. But more importantly we use our skills with numbers to help our clients identify, manage and improve all of the numbers which really matter to them as individuals, their businesses and their lives. We understand that our clients' needs may be complex. These may include the need to maximise their profits, to minimise their tax liabilities, to maximise their wealth or even to rebalance their life-work balance. We know that achieving these and other objectives will take time but we are here for the long term and many of our clients have been engaging with us for a very long time.

As AVN Founder Members we have at our disposal a number of tools and resources to make our clients objectives happen. We also have a great team of individuals who are committed to fully engaging with our clients and helping them achieve their goals.

Why We Are Different

Our most successful clients are the ones who fully engage with us. We find that our Board View sessions can greatly assist in this process. For our premier clients we are able to offer a completely outsourced financial management service so that we become their back office. We will deal with everything from VAT and payroll to management accounting and advice at board level. This is our Virtual Financial Director service and is suitable for entrepreneurs who trust us to do what we do best, enabling them to work on their business rather than in it.

Who We Love To Work With

Our selective approach to taking on clients allows us to work closely with you and helps us to really get to know your business. All of your financial and business requirements will be addressed as we work with you to become your trusted business partner and an indispensable member of your team. We are members of the ICAEW Business Advice Service and provide a wide range of services across accountancy, finance and business.

We offer fixed price agreements for all our services and this will give you peace of mind with no surprise bills. There is no upper limit on the size of business we work with. Although there is no lower limit we only work with clients who are prepared to invest in a minimum fee level. We will work with businesses which are less than 12 months old but they must subscribe to our New Business Start-Up service. The reason for this is that we only want to act for businesses which want to be successful and are prepared to listen to our advice…any business that is not prepared to invest in this service is unlikely to be an ideal client. The only exception is for tax return/income and expenditure only clients. We want to work closely with clients.

WHS Accountants Ltd

AVN Accountant

Leeds, West Yorkshire

Email Graham Sheard **grahams@whsaccountants.co.uk**

Phone **0113 2491101**

Website **www.whsaccountants.co.uk**

About Our Practice

WHS Accountants Ltd is a firm of Chartered Accountants offering a wide range of accountancy and taxation services.

We like to build on your strengths and strengthen your weaknesses. We want your business to reach its maximum potential.

Yet we know that this will only happen if you receive the right advice. So if you are looking for an accounting firm with the expertise to serve as your business advisor, then take a look at WHS Accountants Limited.

Why We Are Different

We are an experienced group of professionals who look beyond the bottom line. That's why we think more like business people than accountants, analysing and consulting with you on complex issues to provide our added insight.

Who We Love To Work With

We act for proprietor controlled businesses across many fields dealing with personal and corporate tax issues as well as offering payroll services.

In particular we act for a large number of dentists, physiotherapists and other health professionals and have expertise in this field.

We are also able to support start up business ventures offering advice and mentoring from our experience.

UWMAccountants
urquhart | warner | myers

Urquhart Warner Myers

AVN Accountant
Leeds, West Yorkshire
Email Jonathan Myers **jm@uwm.co.uk**
Phone **0113 2310202**
Website **www.uwm.co.uk**

About Our Practice

Urquhart Warner Myers is a cutting-edge team of business finance experts with old-fashioned values. Our team boasts a wealth of accounting experience. With over 30 years in the industry and countless accolades, we can proudly say our accounting services are first-class.

Founded in 1978, UWM has grown from a small start-up in Yorkshire to a respected accounting firm with clients across the UK. Over the years, we've helped businesses of every size and from countless industries. Our goal is always the same – to help our clients work towards a better bottom line and achieve their financial goals.

Why We Are Different

We offer clients:

- Help to set business and personal goals and find ways to achieve them
- Install and set up a total Cloud accounting solution
- Take the hassle out of bookkeeping, accounts, payroll, VAT and let the business owner(s) concentrate on what's really important to them in their business
- New ideas that will help their business

Who We Love To Work With

We like to work with business owners who want to grow their business and are looking for accountants who will add something to their business.

Our clients are primarily in the Yorkshire area although technology now allows us to easily communicate with business outside the traditional local area.

Through our expertise in Cloud accounting we can bring huge time and cost savings to businesses who are running their business in the Cloud or want to know where to start.

Find Me An AVN Accountant

Spoiled for choice? There are many accountants to consider.

If you'd like us to put an AVN accountant in touch with you, simply provide us with a little information about yourself including, of course, your contact information. We'll identify an AVN accountant who is appropriate to your needs and preferences.

Simply go to this website **www.avntheaccountants.co.uk** and select the Find an AVN Accountant option from the menu.

What Is AVN?

AVN is an association of UK accountants; accountants who have a common passion for helping UK businesses become the most successful and enjoyable to run in the world.

Many business owners see their accountant as a necessary burden; someone who does what's legally required and nothing more. But that means they miss out on what an accountant can really do for their business by way of the improvements described in this book. AVN helps accountants break the mould.

AVN accountants are making a real and lasting difference to the businesses they work with. I gave just one example of a case study earlier and there are many more in the book, 'The World's Most Inspiring Accountants,' which is full of amazing case studies taken from accountants around the world – many of them AVN accountants in the UK.

Talk To Your Existing Accountant

If you're intrigued by the possibilities within this book my recommendation is that you talk to your current accountant and find out whether or not they can currently offer these types of services. Explain to them that you'd like more help along the lines described in this book.

How To Change Accountant

If your existing accountant isn't able to offer the services I've mentioned in this book then certainly have a conversation with one of the AVN accountants listed here.

You might think that moving accountants is more hassle than it's worth but the reality is that it's quite simple and painless.

Your newly assigned accountant will take on the burden on your behalf with your consent.

Are You An Accountant?

If you'd like to feature in this book, if you'd like to develop your firm in the way I've described in this book and deliver even more value to your clients then go to this website **www.improveyourpractice.co.uk** and get instant access – courtesy of AVN – to a step-by-step programme that delivers incredibly valuable learning and powerful resources to help you improve your profits, cash flow, average fees, service levels and client base.

There are many resources you can download including a copy of the AVN*Excellence* standards I refer to within this book.

In addition, you'll have the opportunity to learn more about AVN and how your accountancy practice and your life could change for the better.

Acknowledgements

The Lewis Ballard case study is taken from the book, 'The World's Most Inspiring Accountants,' by Steve Pipe, Susan Clegg and Shane Lukas. ISBN 978-0-9551007-6-5

About The Author and AVN

Shane Lukas is the Managing Director of AVN. Since 1998 AVN have been training accountants to run more profitable and enjoyable businesses which enable them to regain control of their own lives. We help them deliver greater value to their clients helping them run far more profitable and enjoyable businesses and regain control of their own lives too. Giving accountants a much greater sense of purpose.

Shane is a co-author of the book 'The World's Most Inspiring Accountants' – a book which demonstrates the life changing impact accountants can have on their clients by simply spending more valuable time with them.

Connect with Shane on **Linked in**. linkedin.com/in/slukas